READING AND NOTE TAKING STUDY GUIDE

Prepared by

John Reisbord

BY THE PEOPLE
A HISTORY OF THE UNITED STATES

AP® Edition

James W. Fraser
New York University

PEARSON

Boston Columbus Indianapolis New York San Francisco Upper Saddle River
Amsterdam Cape Town Dubai London Madrid Milan Munich Paris Montréal Toronto
Delhi Mexico City São Paulo Sydney Hong Kong Seoul Singapore Taipei Tokyo

AP® is a trademark registered and/or owned by the College Board, which was not involved in the production of, and does not endorse, this product.

Printed in the United States of America

10 9 8 7 6 5 4 3 2 1

PEARSON

ISBN 10: 0-13-310221-1
ISBN 13: 978-0-13-310221-5

CONTENTS

Fraser: Chapter 1

Complete the following exercises in order *as you read* the chapter.

INTRODUCTION

Introductions provide a valuable guide to the material you are about to read, telling you what topics will be covered and how they fit together. If you keep the "big picture" provided by the introduction in mind as you read the chapter, you'll find it much easier to organize your notes, identify important information, and avoid getting lost in the details. With this in mind, re-read the introduction to Chapter 1. As you read, make a list of the key topics you expect to learn about.

Key Topics

Key Terms

The Peopling of North America

Graphic Note Taking: Compare and Contrast

While the largest and most powerful Pre-Columbian American civilizations were in Mexico and South America, other important societies could be found within the boundaries of the present-day United States. As you read this section, use a table like the one included below to take notes on two such societies: the Anasazi and the Cahokia. As you take notes, be sure to include information on the way climate shaped the development of each culture. You'll use your table to answer a question when you finish this section.

Anasazi	Cahokia

Reviewing the Facts

Provide a short answer (3-4 sentences) for each of the questions below. It's OK if you need to go back and re-read parts of the section in order to find the answers. The purpose of these questions is not to test you, but to help you discover how much you know and what you might need to review.

1. How do modern anthropologists explain the peopling of the Americas?

2. What kind of community did the Anasazi create in Chaco Canyon?

3. What were the key characteristics of Cahokia society?

Making Connections

Take another look at the artist's rendition of Cahokia on page 7 of your textbook. What connections can you make between the layout of the city and Cahokia social and political structures?

Graphic Note Taking: Follow Up

Use your notes to help answer the following question. How did climate shape the growth and development of Cahokia?

The Diverse Communities of the Americas in the 1400s

Graphic Note Taking: Charting Diversity

The Indians of North America were remarkably diverse. They included 500 to 600 independent societies, each with their own traditions, occupations, beliefs, and institutions. As you read this section, use a table like the one included below to take notes on some of the most important of these societies. You'll use your table to answer a question when you finish this section.

	Economy	Society	Culture and Religion
Pueblo People of the Southwest			
Tribes of the Mississippi Valley			
Tribes of the Pacific Coast			
Iroquois and Tribes of the Atlantic Coast			
Aztecs			
Maya			
Inca			

Reviewing the Facts

Provide a short answer (3-4 sentences) for each of the questions below. It's OK if you need to go back and re-read parts of the section in order to find the answers. The purpose of these questions is not to test you, but to help you discover how much you know and what you might need to review.

1. What role did climate play in the decline of Cahokia and the Mound-building culture of the Mississippi Valley?

2. What were the key characteristics of Algonquian society?

3. How did Aztec interactions with other Indian peoples both strengthen and weaken the Aztec empire?

Making Connections

Take another look at the drawing of an Iroquois Onondaga village on page 11 of your text book. What does the drawing tell you about the nature of Iroquois society?

Graphic Note Taking: Follow Up

Use your notes to answer the following question. What role did climate and geography play in creating the social diversity of Indian peoples?

A Changing Europe in the 1400s

Graphic Note Taking: Key Events

The major events and developments of the fourteenth and fifteenth centuries created conditions in Europe that led to overseas expansion. As you read this section, use a table like the one included below to take notes on the most important of these developments. For each event you include, identify the changes the event produced and their significance. You'll use your table to answer a question when you finish this section.

Event:	Importance:

Reviewing the Facts

Provide a short answer (3-4 sentences) for each of the questions below. It's OK if you need to go back and re-read parts of the section in order to find the answers. The purpose of these questions is not to test you, but to help you discover how much you know and what you might need to review.

1. What impact did the Black Death have on late medieval Europe?

2. What were Prince Henry the Navigator's motives for promoting the exploration of the African coast?

3. Why did England and France fail to follow Portugal's example of exploration in the fifteenth century?

Making Connections

Take another look at the painting of European peasants on page 16 of your textbook. In what ways were the people depicted typical Europeans?

Graphic Note Taking: Follow Up

How did the fall of Constantinople to the Ottoman Turks contribute to European westward expansion?

Africa in the 1400s

Graphic Note Taking: Timeline

In the centuries prior to European overseas expansion, West and Central Africa saw the rise and fall of a series of important empires. As you read the section, create a timeline that includes the most important events in the political history of these regions. Your timeline should begin in 1050 with the rise of Mali and end in the 1490 with the conversion of the king of Kongo to Catholicism. You'll use your timeline to answer a question when you finish this section.

Reviewing the Facts

Provide a short answer (3-4 sentences) for each of the questions below. It's OK if you need to go back and re-read parts of the section in order to find the answers. The purpose of these questions is not to test you, but to help you discover how much you know and what you might need to review.

1. What connections were there between Africa and Europe prior to the Portuguese voyages of the fifteenth century?

2. What was the basis of the power of the Kingdom of Ghana?

3. What connection was there between slavery and warfare in fifteenth-century West Africa?

Making Connections

Take another look at Map 1-5: African Trade Networks on page 19 of your textbook. What connections does it suggest between trade routes and the locations of important West African cities?

Graphic Note Taking: Follow Up

Use your timeline to help answer the following question. What role did trade play in the rise and fall of the major West African empires?

Asia in the 1400s

Graphic Note Taking: Outline

Asia was by far the wealthiest and most densely populated region of the world in the fifteenth century. Given this, it's not surprising that Europeans should have been so eager to gain access to Asian trade. As you read this section, create an outline like the one below to help you identify key developments in Asia in the century before European contact with the Americas. You should continue your outline from the point at which the one included below leaves off. You'll use your outline to answer a question when you finish this section.

    I.   Asian Political Organization

         A.   Principle Empires and Kingdoms

              a.   China

                    1. Unified empire

                    2. Population of 150-200 million

Reviewing the Facts

Provide a short answer (3-4 sentences) for each of the questions below. It's OK if you need to go back and re-read parts of the section in order to find the answers. The purpose of these questions is not to test you, but to help you discover how much you know and what you might need to review.

1. How did fifteenth-century Asia differ from the Americas, Africa, and Europe?

2. What role did Emperor Zhu Di play in the history of Chinese exploration?

3. What role did trade play in the societies of Asia, Europe, Africa, and the Americas in the late fifteenth century?

Graphic Note Taking: Follow Up

Why did the Chinese voyages of exploration initiated by Zhu Di come to an end? Use the outline you created while reading this section to help prepare your answer.

Fraser: Chapter 2

Complete the following exercises in order *as you read* the chapter.

INTRODUCTION

Introductions provide a valuable guide to the material you are about to read, telling you what topics will be covered and how they fit together. If you keep the "big picture" provided by the introduction in mind as you read the chapter, you'll find it much easier to organize your notes, identify important information, and avoid getting lost in the details. With this in mind, re-read the introduction to Chapter 2. As you read, make a list of the key topics you expect to learn about.

Key Topics

Key Terms

When you finish reading the chapter, identify and explain the importance of the following terms. Use this list to review your understanding of the chapter.

Columbus, The Columbian Exchange, and Early Conquests

Graphic Note Taking: Identifying Consequences

European contact with the peoples of the Americas was a transformative event, altering life in both Europe and the Americas and reshaping global trade connections and the global balance of power. As you read this section, use a table like the one included below to take notes on the most important consequences of contact. As you take notes, be sure to consider consequences for each category in the Americas, Europe, and the larger world. You'll use your table to answer a question when you finish this section.

Economic consequences:
Political consequences:
Biological consequences:

Reviewing the Facts

Provide a short answer (3-4 sentences) for each of the questions below. It's OK if you need to go back and re-read parts of the section in order to find the answers. The purpose of these questions is not to test you, but to help you discover how much you know and what you might need to review.

1. What motives were behind Columbus's voyages to the New World?

2. What factor played in the largest role in producing the dramatic drop in the native population of the New World that followed the arrival of Europeans?

3. What explains the swiftness of the Spanish conquest of the Aztec and Inca Empires?

Making Connections

Take another look at the image showing the impact of smallpox on Native Americans on page 32 of your text book. Why did smallpox have such a devastating impact on Native American populations?

Graphic Note Taking: Follow Up

Use your notes to help answer the following question. In your opinion, what were the most important consequences of the arrival of Europeans in the New World?

A DIVIDED EUROPE: THE IMPACT OF THE PROTESTANT REFORMATION

Graphic Note Taking: Parallel Developments

The Protestant Reformation and the rise of the nation-state did not proceed from the same causes, but once under way, each had a significant impact on the other. As you read this section, use a table like the one included below to take notes on these two connected developments. You'll use your table to answer a question when you finish this section.

Protestant Reformation:	Emergence of the Nation-State:

Reviewing the Facts

Provide a short answer (3-4 sentences) for each of the questions below. It's OK if you need to go back and re-read parts of the section in order to find the answers. The purpose of these questions is not to test you, but to help you discover how much you know and what you might need to review.

1. What aspects of Catholic practice did Luther challenge?

2. How did the printing press contribute to the spread of Protestantism?

3. How did the 1648 Treaty of Westphalia try to put an end to the religious warfare that had plagued Europe since the mid-sixteenth century?

Making Connections

Take another look at the painting of Martin Luther on page 37 of your text book. What importance should we attach to the fact that he is shown holding a book and a quill?

Graphic Note Taking: Follow Up

Use your notes to answer the following question. Why were national unity and religious uniformity so closely linked in the

EXPLORATION AND ENCOUNTER IN NORTH AMERICA: THE SPANISH

Graphic Note Taking: Key Figures

The conquests of the Aztec and Inca Empires produced enormous wealth for Spain and whetted Spanish appetites for further colonial acquisitions. Consequently, the Spanish sponsored a number of expeditions that explored the regions north of Mexico. As you read this section, use a table like the one included below to take notes on the most important of these expeditions. You'll use your table to answer a question when you finish this section.

Explorer:	Details of Expedition:	Outcome:

Reviewing the Facts

Provide a short answer (3-4 sentences) for each of the questions below. It's OK if you need to go back and re-read parts of the section in order to find the answers. The purpose of these questions is not to test you, but to help you discover how much you know and what you might need to review.

1. Who was Esteban and what role did he play in the Spanish exploration of North America?

2. What were Gaspard de Coligny's motives for establishing a European settlement in Florida?

3. How did the Spanish colonies in Florida differ from those in Mexico and Peru?

Making Connections

Take another look at Map 2-3: North American Exploration on page 40 of your textbook. How does the map help explain the focus of Spanish exploration in North America on the Southwest?

Graphic Note Taking: Follow Up

Why did the Spanish consider the exploration of the lands north of Mexico a failure? Use the table you created while reading this section to help you answer this question.

EXPLORATION AND ENCOUNTER IN NORTH AMERICA: THE FRENCH

Graphic Note Taking: Timeline

The French did not want to leave the Americas to the Spanish or Portuguese, and in the early sixteenth century launched a number of voyages of exploration of their own. As you read the section, create a timeline that includes the most important events in the French exploration of North America. You'll use your timeline to answer a question when you finish this section.

Reviewing the Facts

Provide a short answer (3-4 sentences) for each of the questions below. It's OK if you need to go back and re-read parts of the section in order to find the answers. The purpose of these questions is not to test you, but to help you discover how much you know and what you might need to review.

1. What were the motives behind and goals of the early French exploration of North America?

2. What was the long-term impact of Cartier's voyages to North America on French-Indian relations?

3. What might explain the friendly reception both Cartier and Verrazano received from the Native Americans they encountered?

Making Connections

Take another look at the painting of Jean Ribault's encounter with Timuca Indians on page 45 of your textbook. What details are included in the painting to suggest that the Timuca were friendly?

Graphic Note Taking: Follow Up

Use your timeline to help answer the following question. What was the principle goal of early French exploration of North America?

EXPLORATION AND ENCOUNTER IN NORTH AMERICA: THE ENGLISH

Graphic Note Taking: Outline

England's interest in the Americas grew out of the English Reformation and its subsequent clash with Catholic Spain. As you read this section, create an outline to help you identify the sequence of events that led from England's split with Rome, to its clash with Spain, and finally to its initial presence in the Americas. You should continue your outline from the point at which the one included below leaves off. You'll use your outline to answer a question when you finish this section.

    I.   England's Reformation Shapes the Country

          A. Henry VIII (r. 1509 – 1547)

               a.   Initially a good Catholic

               b.   Pope's denial of annulment led to split

               c.   Parliament made Henry head of the Church of England

               d.   Under Henry, England remained closer to Catholicism than Protestantism

Reviewing the Facts

Provide a short answer (3-4 sentences) for each of the questions below. It's OK if you need to go back and re-read parts of the section in order to find the answers. The purpose of these questions is not to test you, but to help you discover how much you know and what you might need to review.

1. Why did Henry VIII initiate the split between England and the Catholic Church, and how did the Church England differ from the Catholic Church during Henry's reign?

2. After Henry's death, what were the three major religious groups in England, and what did each want?

3. What were England's goals in the Americas during the reign of Elizabeth I?

Making Connections

Take another look at the painting of Elizabeth I on page 50 of your textbook. What details did the artist include to suggest the importance of sea power to sixteenth-century England?

Graphic Note Taking: Follow Up

What connection can you make between the English Reformation and the activities of men like Francis Drake in the late sixteenth century? Use the outline you created while reading this section to help prepare your answer.

Fraser: Chapter 3

Complete the following exercises in order *as you read* the chapter.

INTRODUCTION

Introductions provide a valuable guide to the material you are about to read, telling you what topics will be covered and how they fit together. If you keep the "big picture" provided by the introduction in mind as you read the chapter, you'll find it much easier to organize your notes, identify important information, and avoid getting lost in the details. With this in mind, re-read the introduction to Chapter 3. As you read, make a list of the key topics you expect to learn about.

Key Topics

Key Terms

When you finish reading the chapter, identify and explain the importance of the following terms. Use this list to review your understanding of the chapter.

The English Settle in North America

Graphic Note Taking: Compare and Contrast

Over the course of the seventeenth and eighteenth centuries, British colonial claims in North America expanded dramatically. There was not, however, a single model of development in each British colony. Instead, the colonies varied depending on the circumstances of their creation, the background and goals of their particular colonists, and the economic opportunities presented by their particular environments. As you read this section, use a table like the one included below to take notes on the factors that shaped the development of the various British colonies. You'll use your table to answer a question when you finish this section.

	Circumstances of Settlement	Colonists: Backgrounds and Motives	Economy and Environment
Virginia			
Massachusett			
Maryland			
Connecticut			
New Hampshire			
New York			
Pennsylvania			
Delaware			
Carolina			
Georgia			

Reviewing the Facts

Provide a short answer (3-4 sentences) for each of the questions below. It's OK if you need to go back and re-read parts of the section in order to find the answers. The purpose of these questions is not to test you, but to help you discover how much you know and what you might need to review.

1. How did the advent of commercial tobacco cultivation in Virginia affect the relationship between colonists and Indians?

2. Who were the Puritans and what did they want?

3. How did the establishment of Maryland differ from that of the earlier English colonies?

Making Connections

Take another look at the image of a Virginia tobacco plantation on page 76 of your text book. What important aspects of the emerging Virginia economy does it depict?

Graphic Note Taking: Follow Up

Use your notes to help answer the following question. What role did religion play in shaping the development of the British colonies?

England's Wars, England's Colonies

Graphic Note Taking: Key Developments

Over the course of the seventeenth century, warfare, both in England and in North America, played a key role in shaping the development of the English colonies. As you read this section, make a list of the key conflicts of the seventeenth century. Note details about each conflict, as well as its impact on colonial development. You'll use your list to answer a question when you finish this section.

Reviewing the Facts

Provide a short answer (3-4 sentences) for each of the questions below. It's OK if you need to go back and re-read parts of the section in order to find the answers. The purpose of these questions is not to test you, but to help you discover how much you know and what you might need to review.

1. What events led to the outbreak of the English Civil War?

2. How did English expansion create tension between colonists and Indians in New England?

3. What made Bacon's Rebellion such an important turning point in the history of slavery in Virginia?

Making Connections

Take another look at the map of King Philip's War and Bacon's Rebellion on page 81 of your text book. What forces led to the outbreak of open war between Indians and colonists in New England in 1675?

Graphic Note Taking: Follow Up

Use your notes to answer the following question. What tensions within Virginian society were revealed by Bacon's Rebellion?

France Takes Control of the Heart of a Continent

Graphic Note Taking: Identifying Key Differences

In the second half of the seventeenth century, French interest in the New World intensified. The French grip on its early settlements in the northeast was tightened, and new initiatives brought additional territory under French control. As you read this section, use a table like the one included below to take notes on the three most important regions of French activity in North America. You'll use your table to answer a question when you finish this section.

	Explorers/Settlers	Motives for Exploration/Settlement	Nature of French Presence
Quebec and Montreal			
Mississippi Valley			
Gulf Coast			

Reviewing the Facts

Provide a short answer (3-4 sentences) for each of the questions below. It's OK if you need to go back and re-read parts of the section in order to find the answers. The purpose of these questions is not to test you, but to help you discover how much you know and what you might need to review.

1. What impact did the trade in beaver pelts have on the Indians peoples involved?

2. What parts of North America did Robert de la Salle explore, and what were his goals?

3. What role did African slaves play in shaping the culture and economy of French Louisiana?

Making Connections

Take another look at Map 3-3: France in the American Interior, 1670-1720 on page 84 of your textbook. How would you explain the fact that French exploration concentrated on tracing the course of major rivers?

Graphic Note Taking: Follow Up

What role did competition between France, Spain, and England play in French expansion in North America in the latter half of the seventeenth century? Use the table you created while reading this section to help you answer this question.

Developments in Spanish Colonies North of Mexico

Graphic Note Taking: Outline

Alarmed by French and English initiatives in North America, the Spanish took steps to expand their own holdings and to secure the settlements they already had. As you read the section, create an outline like the one included below to help you trace the most important developments in Spanish North America during the seventeenth and eighteenth centuries. You should continue your outline from the point at which the one included below leaves off. You'll use your outline to answer a question when you finish this section.

    I.   The Great Revolt – New Mexico 1680

          A.   The Pueblo Revolt

               1.   Spanish settlers wiped out and Spanish forced to retreat to Mexico

               2.   Harsh workloads and religious repression sparked revolt

               3.   Santa Fe leveled and Indian life returned to pre-1589 patterns

          B.   The Reestablishment of Spanish Control

               1.

Reviewing the Facts

Provide a short answer (3-4 sentences) for each of the questions below. It's OK if you need to go back and re-read parts of the section in order to find the answers. The purpose of these questions is not to test you, but to help you discover how much you know and what you might need to review.

1. What sparked the Pueblo Revolt of 1680?

2. Who was Don Diego Vargas, and what changes did he implement after the Spanish reestablished control of New Mexico in the early 1690s?

3. Why did the Spanish decide to establish a presence in California, and what form did that presence take?

Making Connections

Take another look at Map 3-5: California Missions on page 88 of your textbook. What does the pattern of Spanish missions suggest about their purpose and the nature of the Spanish presence in California?

Graphic Note Taking: Follow Up

Use your outline to help answer the following question. What role did missionary efforts play in Spanish settlements in North America?

Fraser: Chapter 4

Complete the following exercises in order *as you read* the chapter.

INTRODUCTION

Introductions provide a valuable guide to the material you are about to read, telling you what topics will be covered and how they fit together. If you keep the "big picture" provided by the introduction in mind as you read the chapter, you'll find it much easier to organize your notes, identify important information, and avoid getting lost in the details. With this in mind, re-read the introduction to Chapter 4. As you read, make a list of the key topics you expect to learn about.

Key Topics

Key Terms

England's Glorious Revolution and "The Rights of Englishmen," 1689

Graphic Note Taking: Compare and Contrast

The events of the Glorious Revolution were not confined to England, nor were its consequences. In the aftermath of the revolution, many colonists had a new sense of their rights as Englishmen and of their relationship to the British government. As you read this section, use a table like the one included below to take notes on key aspects of British rule under James II and under William and Mary. You'll use your table to answer a question when you finish this section.

James II	William and Mary

Reviewing the Facts

Provide a short answer (3-4 sentences) for each of the questions below. It's OK if you need to go back and re-read parts of the section in order to find the answers. The purpose of these questions is not to test you, but to help you discover how much you know and what you might need to review.

1. What policies brought James II and Parliament into conflict and ultimately led to his ousting?

2. How did John Locke justify the Glorious Revolution?

3. How did society and government in the British colonies change after the Glorious Revolution?

Making Connections

Take another look at the page from a colonial newspaper on page 95 of your text book. What might explain the growing popularity of such publications in the eighteenth century?

Graphic Note Taking: Follow Up

Use your notes to help answer the following questions. How did British rule of the North American colonies change with the ascension of William and Mary to the throne?

The Plantation World: From a Society with Slaves to a Slave Society

Graphic Note Taking: Common Experiences

After Bacon's Rebellion, a major shift took place in the southern colonies. What had been societies with slaves became societies in which the institution of slavery dominated all aspects of life. As you read this section, use a table like the one included below to take notes of the experiences of victims of the Atlantic slave trade, from enslavement in Africa to forced labor in the Americas. You'll use your table to help you answer a question when you finish this section.

Enslavement
The Middle Passage
Life in the Americas

Reviewing the Facts

Provide a short answer (3-4 sentences) for each of the questions below. It's OK if you need to go back and re-read parts of the section in order to find the answers. The purpose of these questions is not to test you, but to help you discover how much you know and what you might need to review.

1. How did the relationship between slavery and race change in the late seventeenth and early eighteenth centuries?

2. What kind of life could plantation slaves expect after the 1680s?

3. Why was it in the interests of Spanish authorities to encourage Carolina slaves to escape to Florida?

Making Connections

Take another look at map 4-1: Enslaved People in British North America in 1750 on page 97 of your text book. What percentage of the population of the Lower South were slaves? What about the North? How would you explain this difference?

Graphic Note Taking: Follow Up

Use your notes to answer the following question. What factors contributed to rapid expansion of the Atlantic slave trade in the late seventeenth and early eighteenth centuries?

Stability and Instability in American and British Worlds

Graphic Note Taking: Identifying Key Changes

As Britain's economic power grew and the colonies in North America matured, life changed in Britain and the colonies, changes that brought both new prosperity and new tensions. As you read this section, use a table like the one included below to take notes on the most important trends in the British colonies in the first half of the eighteenth century. You'll use your table to answer a question when you finish this section.

Cities and Urban Life
Economic Structures and Attitudes
Social Developments
Religious Life

Reviewing the Facts

Provide a short answer (3-4 sentences) for each of the questions below. It's OK if you need to go back and re-read parts of the section in order to find the answers. The purpose of these questions is not to test you, but to help you discover how much you know and what you might need to review.

1. Why were the lives of many women in colonial America isolated and lonely?

2. What did mercantilists believe, and how did their views shape British policy?

3. How did the wars of the 1700s shape the way British colonists saw their relationship to the British government?

Making Connections

Take another look at illustration of the powers of witches on page 103 of your textbook. What tensions and anxieties in colonial society were reflected in images such as this one?

Graphic Note Taking: Follow Up

What new social attitudes emerged in the mid-eighteenth century? Why did they emerge? Use the table you created while reading this section to help you answer this question.

Fraser: Chapter 5

Complete the following exercises in order *as you read* the chapter.

INTRODUCTION

Introductions provide a valuable guide to the material you are about to read, telling you what topics will be covered and how they fit together. If you keep the "big picture" provided by the introduction in mind as you read the chapter, you'll find it much easier to organize your notes, identify important information, and avoid getting lost in the details. With this in mind, re-read the introduction to Chapter 5. As you read, make a list of the key topics you expect to learn about.

Key Topics

Key Terms

When you finish reading the chapter, identify and explain the importance of the following terms. Use this list to review your understanding of the chapter.

Prelude to Revolution

Graphic Note Taking: Identifying Consequences

The world war that raged between 1754 and 1763, pitting Britain against France, had profound consequences for British North America. Victory made the British the dominant power on the continent, but it also produced new problems and challenges for the British government. As you read this section, use a table like the one included below to take notes on the most important consequences of British victory. You'll use your table to answer a question when you finish this section.

Political and Diplomatic Consequences	
Fiscal Consequences	
Consequences for Colonist/Indian Relations	

Reviewing the Facts

Provide a short answer (3-4 sentences) for each of the questions below. It's OK if you need to go back and re-read parts of the section in order to find the answers. The purpose of these questions is not to test you, but to help you discover how much you know and what you might need to review.

1. How did the French and Indian War enhance British power around the world?

2. How did the way British colonists viewed Indian peoples change after 1763?

3. Why did British officials seek to increase colonial taxes and duties in the years following the French and Indian War?

Making Connections

Take another look at the painting of the Mohawk chief Hendrick on page 128 of your text book. Why might an Indian leader like Hendrick have chosen to ally himself with the British?

Graphic Note Taking: Follow Up

Use your notes to help answer the following question. Why was British victory in the French and Indian War a disaster for Indian peoples?

"The Revolution Was in the Minds of the People"

Graphic Note Taking: Timeline

The twelve years between the end of the French and Indian War and the battles of Lexington and Concord were eventful ones, as British policy makers sought to increase colonial revenues in the face of escalating resistance. As you read this section, create a timeline of key events to help you trace the path towards war between Britain and its North American colonies. You'll use your timeline to help you answer a question when you finish this section.

Reviewing the Facts

Provide a short answer (3-4 sentences) for each of the questions below. It's OK if you need to go back and re-read parts of the section in order to find the answers. The purpose of these questions is not to test you, but to help you discover how much you know and what you might need to review.

1. What were the most important intellectual influences on the political thought of the advocates of American independence?

2. How and why did British efforts to increase revenues, as well as the level of colonial resistance to such efforts, escalate in the 1760s and 1770s?

3. How did British Indian policy contribute to the rising tensions between the British government and its colonial subjects?

Making Connections

Take another look at the engraving of Phillis Wheatley page 138 of your text book. How did free African Americans like Wheatley view the growing conflict between Britain and the colonies?

Graphic Note Taking: Follow Up

Use your notes to answer the following question. In your opinion, was there a moment between 1763 and 1775 when a war for independence became inevitable? If so, when did that moment occur?

The War for Independence

Graphic Note Taking: Mastering Details

Starting in 1775, events on the battle field dominated the drive for American independence. As you read this section, take notes using a table like the one included below to help you master the outcomes and impact of the most important battles of the war. You'll use your table to answer a question when you finish this section.

Battle	Outcome	Consequences

Reviewing the Facts

Provide a short answer (3-4 sentences) for each of the questions below. It's OK if you need to go back and re-read parts of the section in order to find the answers. The purpose of these questions is not to test you, but to help you discover how much you know and what you might need to review.

1. How did enslaved African Americans respond to the British promise to emancipate slaves who ran away and joined the British army? What role did such slaves play in the war?

2. What arguments did Thomas Paine put forward in *Common Sense*? What impact did the pamphlet

3. What was the importance of the Battle of Saratoga?

Making Connections

Take another look at the painting of Sarah Franklin Bache on page 150 of your textbook. What role did women like Bache play in supporting the patriot cause?

Graphic Note Taking: Follow Up

In your opinion, what was the most important battle of the war? Why? Use the table you created while reading this section to help you answer this question.

Fraser: Chapter 6

Complete the following exercises in order *as you read* the chapter.

INTRODUCTION

Introductions provide a valuable guide to the material you are about to read, telling you what topics will be covered and how they fit together. If you keep the "big picture" provided by the introduction in mind as you read the chapter, you'll find it much easier to organize your notes, identify important information, and avoid getting lost in the details. With this in mind, re-read the introduction to Chapter 6. As you read, make a list of the key topics you expect to learn about.

Key Topics

Key Terms

When you finish reading the chapter, identify and explain the importance of the following terms. Use this list to review your understanding of the chapter.

The State of the Nation at War's End

Graphic Note Taking: Charting Diverse Outcomes

When the War for Independence officially came to an end in 1783, newly independent Americans from all walks of life celebrated. Victory, however, had very different consequences for different social and ethnic groups. As you read this section, use a table like the one included below to take notes on the impact of the American victory on important segments of colonial society. You'll use your table to answer a question when you finish this section.

Group	Consequences
Revolutionary Army Officers	
Poor White Farmers	
White Settlers Moving West	
American Indians	
Slaves, former Slaves, and Slave Owners	
Women	

Reviewing the Facts

Provide a short answer (3-4 sentences) for each of the questions below. It's OK if you need to go back and re-read parts of the section in order to find the answers. The purpose of these questions is not to test you, but to help you discover how much you know and what you might need to review.

1. What brought the American army to the brink of mutiny and a *coup d'état* in 1783?

2. Why was American victory in the Revolutionary War a disaster for American Indians?

3. What role did advocates of Republican Motherhood imagine women playing in the new nation?

Making Connections

Take another look at the drawing of discontented farmers gathering during Shays's Rebellion on page 160 of your text book. How might such scenes have contributed to the push to replace the Articles of Confederation with a document that established a stronger central government?

Graphic Note Taking: Follow Up

Use your notes to help answer the following question. What impact did American victory in the Revolutionary War have on the institution of slavery?

Creating a Government: Writing the U.S. Constitution

Graphic Note Taking: Outline

By the late 1780s, many Americans had become convinced that the nation's problems could not be adequately addressed by the government established by the Articles of Confederation. Facing complex fiscal and national security challenges, delegates met in Philadelphia in 1787 to craft a new constitution. As you read the section, create an outline like the one included below to help you trace the developments and debates that led to the ratification of the U.S. Constitution. You should continue your outline from the point at which the one included below leaves off. You'll use your outline to answer a question when you finish this section.

I. The Crisis of the 1780s: The Failure of the Articles of Confederation

    A. Challenges and Problems

        1. The power of state governments

        2. Limits on ability of national government to act in unified fashion

        3. Unanimous agreement required to levy taxes

Reviewing the Facts

Provide a short answer (3-4 sentences) for each of the questions below. It's OK if you need to go back and re-read parts of the section in order to find the answers. The purpose of these questions is not to test you, but to help you discover how much you know and what you might need to review.

1. What was the key difference between the Virginia Plan and the New Jersey Plan?

2. What concessions were made to slaveholders during the drafting of the Constitution?

3. Who were the Antifederalists?

Making Connections

Take another look at the image of crowds celebrating the ratification of the Constitution on page 182 of your text book. Given the strong opposition to the Constitution in many parts of the country, how would you explain the positive popular reaction to ratification?

Graphic Note Taking: Follow Up

Use your notes to answer the following question. Why did the Federalists win the battle over the ratification of the Constitution?

Fraser: Chapter 7

Complete the following exercises in order *as you read* the chapter.

INTRODUCTION

Introductions provide a valuable guide to the material you are about to read, telling you what topics will be covered and how they fit together. If you keep the "big picture" provided by the introduction in mind as you read the chapter, you'll find it much easier to organize your notes, identify important information, and avoid getting lost in the details. With this in mind, re-read the introduction to Chapter 7. As you read, make a list of the key topics you expect to learn about.

Key Topics

Key Terms

When you finish reading the chapter, identify and explain the importance of the following terms. Use this list to review your understanding of the chapter.

Convening a Congress, Inaugurating a President, Adopting a Bill of Rights

Graphic Note Taking: Mastering Details

The ratification of the Constitution set the stage for the creation of a new federal government. There was much to do, including holding elections, creating the executive branch, and enacting the Bill of Rights. As you read this section, make a list of the most important early actions of the newly formed federal government. Note both the action and its significance. You'll use your list to answer a question when you finish this section.

1.

2.

3.

4.

5.

Reviewing the Facts

Provide a short answer (3-4 sentences) for each of the questions below. It's OK if you need to go back and re-read parts of the section in order to find the answers. The purpose of these questions is not to test you, but to help you discover how much you know and what you might need to review.

1. What urgent tasks did Congress have to address as soon as it convened in early 1789?

2. What suggestions were made for the style and tone of presidency? What approach did Washington choose?

3. Why did Madison move quickly to create a Bill of Rights, despite the fact that he did not personally believe the Constitution needed amending?

Making Connections

Take another look at the drawing of a Methodist church on page 188 of your text book. Why might the members of such a church have supported the strict separation of church and state?

Graphic Note Taking: Follow Up

Use your notes to help answer the following question. What limits did the Bill of Rights place on the powers of the federal government?

Creating an Economy: Alexander Hamilton and the U.S. Economic System

Graphic Note Taking: Compare and Contrast

As the federal government grappled with the many economic problems facing the nation, competing visions of the nation's economic future emerged among the country's leaders. These competing visions, represented by the ideas of Alexander Hamilton and Thomas Jefferson, would help define the lines of the developing party system. As you read this section, use a table like the one included below to take notes on Hamilton and Jefferson's key ideas. You'll use your table to answer a question when you finish this section.

Alexander Hamilton	Thomas Jefferson

Reviewing the Facts

Provide a short answer (3-4 sentences) for each of the questions below. It's OK if you need to go back and re-read parts of the section in order to find the answers. The purpose of these questions is not to test you, but to help you discover how much you know and what you might need to review.

1. Why was it essential for Hamilton to address the national debt?

2. What groups opposed the recommendations made by Hamilton in his *Report Relative to a Provision for the Support of Public Credit*? What was the basis of their opposition?

3. What advantages did Hamilton see in the establishment of a central bank?

Making Connections

Take another look at the image of the First Bank of the United States on page 192 of your text book. What does its design suggest about Hamilton's vision of the new bank?

Graphic Note Taking: Follow Up

Use your notes to answer the following question. Why did Jefferson reject the proposals made by Hamilton in his *Report on Manufacturers*?

Setting the Pace: The Washington Administration

Graphic Note Taking: Identifying Challenges

The establishment of a government under the terms of the Constitution did not bring peace and stability to the new nation. As president, George Washington was faced with a number of serious threats to the unity and security of the United States. As you read this section, use a table like the one to identify those threats and describe Washington's response to them. You'll use your table to answer a question when you finish this section.

Threat	Washington's Response

Reviewing the Facts

Provide a short answer (3-4 sentences) for each of the questions below. It's OK if you need to go back and re-read parts of the section in order to find the answers. The purpose of these questions is not to test you, but to help you discover how much you know and what you might need to review.

1. Why was the Treaty of Greenville such an important turning point in relations between white settlers and Indian peoples in the Ohio Valley?

2. Why did Hamilton's Whiskey Tax spark a rebellion led by western farmers?

3. How did Citizen Genet anger President Washington and dim popular enthusiasm for the French Revolution among some Americans?

Making Connections

Take another look at the image of the tarring and feathering of a U.S. tax agent on page 200 of your text book. What connections can you make between this image and similar images of attacks on tax agents created before and during the Revolutionary War?

Graphic Note Taking: Follow Up

Use your notes to answer the following question. How did Washington respond to the challenges posed?

The Birth of Political Parties: Adams and Jefferson

Graphic Note Taking: Outline

The framers of the Constitution feared political factions and took steps to avoid their formation. Nonetheless, by the mid-1790s political divisions that would evolve into political parties were already starting to emerge. As you read this section, create an outline like the one below to help you trace the development of American politics in the late eighteenth century. You should continue your outline from the point at which the one included below leaves off. You'll use your outline to answer a question when you finish this section.

    I.   The Election of 1796

          A.   John Adams Versus Thomas Jefferson

                1.   Adams represented the Federalists, Jefferson the anti-federalists

                2.   Candidates did not campaign in person

                3.   Many saw Washington as offering unofficial support for Adams

Reviewing the Facts

Provide a short answer (3-4 sentences) for each of the questions below. It's OK if you need to go back and re-read parts of the section in order to find the answers. The purpose of these questions is not to test you, but to help you discover how much you know and what you might need to review.

1. What were the most important consequences of the "XYZ Affair"?

2. What were the Alien and Sedition Acts, and who did they target?

3. What constitutional claims were made in the Kentucky and Virginia Resolutions?

Making Connections

Take another look at the cartoon depicting French government on page 207 of your text book. What importance should we attach to the fact that the French are depicted as having close relations with Africans and Indians?

Graphic Note Taking: Follow Up

Use your outline to answer the following question. How did the elections of 1796 and 1800 differ?

Fraser: Chapter 8

Complete the following exercises in order *as you read* the chapter.

INTRODUCTION

Introductions provide a valuable guide to the material you are about to read, telling you what topics will be covered and how they fit together. If you keep the "big picture" provided by the introduction in mind as you read the chapter, you'll find it much easier to organize your notes, identify important information, and avoid getting lost in the details. With this in mind, re-read the introduction to Chapter 8. As you read, make a list of the key topics you expect to learn about.

Key Topics

Key Terms

When you finish reading the chapter, identify and explain the importance of the following terms. Use this list to review your understanding of the chapter.

Jefferson and the Republican Ideal

Graphic Note Taking: Mastering Details

Thomas Jefferson's vision of the United States and its future had a lasting impact on American life. As you read this section, use a table like the one included below to take notes on Jefferson's most important assumptions and beliefs. Be sure to include details about how those beliefs were translated into actions and policies. You'll use your list to answer a question when you finish this section.

Social Hierarchy
The American Economy
The Role of Government
Individual Rights and Liberties

Reviewing the Facts

Provide a short answer (3-4 sentences) for each of the questions below. It's OK if you need to go back and re-read parts of the section in order to find the answers. The purpose of these questions is not to test you, but to help you discover how much you know and what you might need to review.

1. What steps did Jefferson take to reduce the size of the federal government?

2. What was the long-term importance of the Supreme Court's decision in *Marbury v. Madison*?

3. How did the makeup of the American electorate change in the early nineteenth century?

Making Connections

Take another look at the painting of Monticello on page 227 of your text book. How well does Jefferson's home reflect his political values?

Graphic Note Taking: Follow Up

Use your notes to help answer the following question. What connections can you make between Jefferson's political ideology and his domestic policy initiatives?

The Ideal of Religious Freedom

Graphic Note Taking: Charting Diversity

The religious revival of the 1820s and 1830s, the Second Great Awakening had a profound impact on American life and culture. As state-sponsored churches disappeared, they were replaced by dynamic and diverse denominations. As you read this section, use a table like the one included below to take notes on America's religious diversity in the early nineteenth century. You'll use your table to answer a question when you finish this section.

Methodists
Baptists
Free Black Churches   ]
Religion and Slavery
Catholics
Jews

Reviewing the Facts

Provide a short answer (3-4 sentences) for each of the questions below. It's OK if you need to go back and re-read parts of the section in order to find the answers. The purpose of these questions is not to test you, but to help you discover how much you know and what you might need to review.

1. How did the place of religion in American life change between 1775 and 1840?

2. What made John Wesley's Methodism appealing to so many Americans?

3. How did the Second Great Awakening affect enslaved African-Americans?

Making Connections

Take another look at the drawing of a camp revival meeting on page 236 of your text book. How would

Graphic Note Taking: Follow Up

Use your notes to answer the following question. What common beliefs connected participants in the Second Great Awakening?

Beyond the Mississippi: The Louisiana Purchase and the Expedition of Lewis and Clark

Graphic Note Taking: Outline

Jefferson's presidency saw the dramatic expansion of American territory, with the Louisiana Purchase almost doubling the nation's land area. As you read the section, create an outline like the one included below to help you trace the events that led to the Louisiana Purchase, as well as the initial efforts to explore and survey the new territory. You should continue your outline from the point at which the one included below leaves off. You'll use your outline to answer a question when you finish this section.

I.

    A.

        1.

        2.

        3.

Reviewing the Facts

Provide a short answer (3-4 sentences) for each of the questions below. It's OK if you need to go back and re-read parts of the section in order to find the answers. The purpose of these questions is not to test you, but to help you discover how much you know and what you might need to review.

1. Why was New Orleans so important to the United States?

2. How did New Orleans differ from other American cities of the early nineteenth century?

3. Why did Jefferson authorize the Lewis and Clark expedition?

Making Connections

Take another look at Map 8-1 Exploring the New Territory on page 236 of your text book. What role did Indian peoples and individual Indians play in the success of the Lewis and Clark expedition?

Graphic Note Taking: Follow Up

Use your notes to answer the following question. Why did Napoleon decide to sell the Louisiana Territory to the United States?

The War of 1812

Graphic Note Taking: Timeline

The War of 1812 had deep roots, going back to the Revolution itself. Tensions between the United States and Britain never really subsided after the War for Independence, and in 1812 they exploded in a new conflict. As you read this section, create a time line of key events leading to the outbreak of war. Your timeline should start in 1783 with the Treaty of Paris and end in 1815 with the Battle of New Orleans.

Reviewing the Facts

Provide a short answer (3-4 sentences) for each of the questions below. It's OK if you need to go back and re-read parts of the section in order to find the answers. The purpose of these questions is not to test you, but to help you discover how much you know and what you might need to review.

1. What was the Embargo Act and why did it fail to achieve its desired results?

2. Who were the War Hawks and what did they want?

3. Why did the British agree to a peace treaty that affirmed the pre-war status quo, despite the fact that they were winning the war?

Making Connections

Take another look at the paintings of Tecumseh and Tenskwatawa on page 240 of your text book. What

Graphic Note Taking: Follow Up

Use your timeline to answer the following question. What were the root causes of the War of 1812?

Expanding American Territory and Influence

Graphic Note Taking: Outline

American expansion did not end with the Louisiana Purchase. Under Jefferson's successors, the United States acquired additional territory, more white settlers moved west, and the United States asserted its dominance in the Western Hemisphere. As you read this section, create an outline like the one included below to help you trace these developments. You should continue your outline from the point at which the one included below leaves off. You'll use your outline to answer a question when you finish this section.

I.   Moving Beyond America's Borders

     A.   Kentucky and Missouri

          1.   Daniel Boone: created first white settlements in Kentucky, later moved to Spanish-controlled Missouri

          2.   Settlers assumed that where they went, American sovereignty would follow

          3.   Boone's pattern followed in Florida, Texas, New Mexico and California

Reviewing the Facts

Provide a short answer (3-4 sentences) for each of the questions below. It's OK if you need to go back and re-read parts of the section in order to find the answers. The purpose of these questions is not to test you, but to help you discover how much you know and what you might need to review.

1. Why was the United States interested in gaining control of Florida?

2. Why did the Spanish agree to transfer control of Florida to the United States?

3. What implicit claims did the United States make in issuing the Monroe Doctrine?

Making Connections

Take another look at the drawing of the Russian settlement in Sitka, Alaska, on page 248 of your text book. What other nations competed with the United States for control of North America?

Graphic Note Taking: Follow Up

Use your outline to answer the following question. What role did ordinary Americans play in the territorial expansion of the early nineteenth century?

Fraser: Chapter 9

Complete the following exercises in order *as you read* the chapter.

INTRODUCTION

Introductions provide a valuable guide to the material you are about to read, telling you what topics will be covered and how they fit together. If you keep the "big picture" provided by the introduction in mind as you read the chapter, you'll find it much easier to organize your notes, identify important information, and avoid getting lost in the details. With this in mind, re-read the introduction to Chapter 9. As you read, make a list of the key topics you expect to learn about.

Key Topics

Key Terms

When you finish reading the chapter, identify and explain the importance of the following terms. Use this list to review your understanding of the chapter.

Creating the Cotton Economy

Graphic Note Taking: Mastering Details

The impact of the emergence of the cotton economy was not limited to southern slaveholders and their human property. The boom in cotton cultivation that took place in the early nineteenth century contributed to industrialization in the North and changed the economic relationship between the United States and Europe. As you read this section, use a table like the one included below to take notes on the many consequences of cotton's growing importance. You'll use your table to answer a question when you finish this section.

Social and Economic Impact in the South
Social and Economic Impact in the North
The United States and the International Marketplace

Reviewing the Facts

Provide a short answer (3-4 sentences) for each of the questions below. It's OK if you need to go back and re-read parts of the section in order to find the answers. The purpose of these questions is not to test you, but to help you discover how much you know and what you might need to review.

1. How did the cotton gin transform the American economy?

2. What made factory work attractive to young women living in rural New England in the early nineteenth century?

3. What advantages allowed New York to play a dominant role in the nineteenth-century cotton economy?

Making Connections

Take another look at the picture of slaves picking cotton on page 258 of your text book. What connections can you make between the spread of cotton cultivation and the spread of slavery?

Graphic Note Taking: Follow Up

Use your notes to help answer the following question. How did cotton change the nature of American slavery?

Commerce, Technology, and Transportation

Graphic Note Taking: The Social and Economic Impact of the Transportation Revolution

The emergence of the market economy and the growing integration of the United States into existing systems of global commerce depended on the improvements in internal transportation. As you read this section, use a table like the one included below to take notes on the way transportation innovations transformed America's economy and society. You'll use your table to answer a question when you finish this section.

	Social and Economic Impact
Canals	
Steamboats	
Roads	

Reviewing the Facts

Provide a short answer (3-4 sentences) for each of the questions below. It's OK if you need to go back and re-read parts of the section in order to find the answers. The purpose of these questions is not to test you, but to help you discover how much you know and what you might need to review.

1. How did steamboats transform trade on the Mississippi River?

2. What role did the federal government play in expanding America's road system?

3. What role did banks play in the early nineteenth-century American economy?

Making Connections

Take another look at the drawing of a lumber mill on page 272 of your text book. How did the operation pictured here differ from its counterparts fifty years earlier?

Graphic Note Taking: Follow Up

Use your notes to answer the following question. What impact did the Erie Canal have on the American economy?

From the Era of Good Feelings to the Politics of Division

Graphic Note Taking: Outline

On the surface, the 1820s were a period of relative national unanimity. However, as the decade came to a close it was clear that were deep political divisions within the country, divisions that would only intensify in the decades to come. As you read the section, create an outline like the one included below to help you trace the political developments of the 1820s. You should continue your outline from the point at which the one included below leaves off. You'll use your outline to answer a question when you finish this section.

    I.   The Supreme Court Defines Its Place

          A.   The Marshall Court

              1. *Dartmouth College v. Woodward* (1819), inviolability of contracts

              2. *McCulloch v. Maryland* (1819), prevented states from interfering with the workings of the federal government

              3. *Gibbons v. Ogden* (1824), prevented states from interfering with interstate commerce

Reviewing the Facts

Provide a short answer (3-4 sentences) for each of the questions below. It's OK if you need to go back and re-read parts of the section in order to find the answers. The purpose of these questions is not to test you, but to help you discover how much you know and what you might need to review.

1. How did the Missouri Compromise propose to resolve the issue of the expansion of slavery?

2. How did Henry Clay believe his "American System" would benefit the country?

3. What role did the press play in the election of 1828?

Making Connections

Take another look at drawing of Andrew Jackson speaking to a crowd on page 282 of your text book.

Graphic Note Taking: Follow Up

Use your notes to answer the following question. What were the most important differences between the Whig Party and the Democratic Party of the late 1820s?

Fraser: Chapter 10

Complete the following exercises in order *as you read* the chapter.

INTRODUCTION

Introductions provide a valuable guide to the material you are about to read, telling you what topics will be covered and how they fit together. If you keep the "big picture" provided by the introduction in mind as you read the chapter, you'll find it much easier to organize your notes, identify important information, and avoid getting lost in the details. With this in mind, re-read the introduction to Chapter 10. As you read, make a list of the key topics you expect to learn about.

Key Topics

Key Terms

When you finish reading the chapter, identify and explain the importance of the following terms. Use this list to review your understanding of the chapter.

Jacksonian Democracy, Jacksonian Government

Graphic Note Taking: Charting Jackson's Domestic Agenda

Andrew Jackson came to office with clear sense of his political agenda. Over the course of his two terms in office, Jackson achieved much of what he set out to accomplish, profoundly influencing the development of American government and politics in the process. As you read this section, use a table like the one included below to take notes on Jackson's agenda. You'll use your table to answer a question when you finish this section.

	Beliefs and Goals	Policies
The Powers of the President		
Indian Removal		
The Second Bank of the United States		
Tariffs and Nullification		

Reviewing the Facts

Provide a short answer (3-4 sentences) for each of the questions below. It's OK if you need to go back and re-read parts of the section in order to find the answers. The purpose of these questions is not to test you, but to help you discover how much you know and what you might need to review.

1. What options were the Cherokees given under the terms of the Indian Removal Act?

2. What groups opposed the Second Bank of the United States? What was the basis of their opposition?

3. On what grounds did John C. Calhoun claim that South Carolina could refuse to enforce a federal law?

Making Connections

Take another look at the picture of the crowd outside the White House after Jackson's inauguration on page 287 of your text book. How might a Jackson supporter have responded to this image? How about a Jackson opponent?

Graphic Note Taking: Follow Up

Use your notes to help answer the following question. Why was Jackson determined to destroy the Second Bank of the United States?

Democratized Religion: The Second Great Awakening

Graphic Note Taking: Identifying Key Figures

The religious revival of the 1820s and 1830s brought a number of spiritual leaders to the forefront of American life. These men and women played an important role in shaping not only the nation's religious attitudes, but its social and political attitudes as well. As you read this section, make a list of prominent religious figures. Make a note of the activities and beliefs of each figure you include. You'll use your list to help answer a question when you finish this section.

1.

2.

3.

Reviewing the Facts

Provide a short answer (3-4 sentences) for each of the questions below. It's OK if you need to go back and re-read parts of the section in order to find the answers. The purpose of these questions is not to test you, but to help you discover how much you know and what you might need to review.

1. How did the new religious organizations and societies that were formed in the 1820s and 1830s differ from earlier such bodies?

2. What reform movements grew out of the Second Great Awakening?

3. Why was America of the 1820s and 1830s fertile ground for the formation of radical social experiments and utopian religious communities?

Making Connections

Take another look at the illustration from an anti-alcohol publication on page 304 of your text book. What lessons did the illustrator hope viewers would take away from this scene?

Graphic Note Taking: Follow Up

Use your notes to answer the following question. What shared beliefs united many of the leaders of the Second Great Awakening?

Democratized Education: The Birth of the Common School

Graphic Note Taking: Outline

Andrew Jackson may have dominated American politics in the late 1820s and early 1830s, but the transformation of the nation's public school system during this period reflected the goals and beliefs of his opponent. As you read the section, create an outline like the one included below to help you trace the development of public education in United States. You should continue your outline from the point at which the one included below leaves off. You'll use your outline to answer a question when you finish this section.

    I.   The Birth of the Common School

          A.   Women Become Teachers

                1.   Reformers linked the desirability of female teachers to women's "natural roles"

                2.   New schools opened to train female teachers

                3.   Reformers believed women should get the same educational opportunities as men

Reviewing the Facts

Provide a short answer (3-4 sentences) for each of the questions below. It's OK if you need to go back and re-read parts of the section in order to find the answers. The purpose of these questions is not to test you, but to help you discover how much you know and what you might need to review.

1. Why did Catherine Beecher believe it was so important to train young women to become teachers?

2. What were the key components of Horace Mann's program of educational reform?

3. Why were many Roman Catholics hostile to Horace Mann's reforms?

Making Connections

Take another look at the painting of an early nineteenth-century school on page 308 of your text book. In what ways was the school depicted in this painting typical of schools of the era?

Graphic Note Taking: Follow Up

Use your notes to answer the following question. What groups offered the strongest support for the kinds of educational reforms advocated by Horace Mann and his allies? What groups opposed Mann's reforms? Why?

Fraser: Chapter 11

Complete the following exercises in order *as you read* the chapter.

INTRODUCTION

Introductions provide a valuable guide to the material you are about to read, telling you what topics will be covered and how they fit together. If you keep the "big picture" provided by the introduction in mind as you read the chapter, you'll find it much easier to organize your notes, identify important information, and avoid getting lost in the details. With this in mind, re-read the introduction to Chapter 11. As you read, make a list of the key topics you expect to learn about.

Key Topics

Key Terms

When you finish reading the chapter, identify and explain the importance of the following terms. Use this list to review your understanding of the chapter.

Manifest Destiny: The Importance of an Idea

Graphic Note Taking: Charting Conflict

Proponents of Manifest Destiny liked to imagine the West as an empty space, a place into which Americans and American culture could spread without hindrance. In fact, another nation, Mexico, had already claimed much of the region. As you read this section, use a table like the one included below to take notes on the conflicts between Americans and Mexicans in Texas and California in the first half of the nineteenth century. You'll use your table to answer a question when you finish this section.

	Texas	California
Mexican Presence		
American Presence		
Sources of Conflict		

Reviewing the Facts

Provide a short answer (3-4 sentences) for each of the questions below. It's OK if you need to go back and re-read parts of the section in order to find the answers. The purpose of these questions is not to test you, but to help you discover how much you know and what you might need to review.

1. What sparked the revolts that culminated in the formation of the Republic of Texas in 1836?

2. What goals did the Spanish have for the missions they established in California in the late eighteenth century?

3. What led to the Panic of 1837?

Making Connections

Take another look at the painting showing white settlers moving west on page 316 of your text book. What message might the artist have been attempting to convey with this image?

Graphic Note Taking: Follow Up

Use your notes to help answer the following question. Why was the United States government reluctant to annex Texas in 1836?

The U.S. War with Mexico, 1846-1848

Graphic Note Taking: Outline

From the moment he became president, James Polk was determined to enlarge Texas and to acquire New Mexico and California by any means necessary. When Mexico refused his demands, he looked for, and found, a pretext to go to war. As you read the section, create an outline like the one included below to help you trace the course of the Mexican-American War. You'll use your outline to answer a question when you finish this section.

I. The Mexican-American War

    A. Finding a Pretext for War

        1. Polk claimed the Rio Grande as the western border of Texas

        2. At the same time that Polk negotiated with Mexico, he sent U.S. troops across the Sabine River

        3. A clash between U.S. and Mexican troops near the Rio Grande provided an excuse for a declaration of war

Reviewing the Facts

Provide a short answer (3-4 sentences) for each of the questions below. It's OK if you need to go back and re-read parts of the section in order to find the answers. The purpose of these questions is not to test you, but to help you discover how much you know and what you might need to review.

1. How and why did the initial diversity of the California gold fields give way to a racially homogenous miner population?

2. Why did demand for whale products increase in the first half of the nineteenth century?

3. How and why did the United States "open up" Japan in the 1850s?

Making Connections

Take another look at the painting entitled *War News from Mexico* on page 330 of your text book. How would you explain the artist's inclusion of two African-Americans, most likely slaves, in the bottom right corner of the painting?

Graphic Note Taking: Follow Up

Use your notes to answer the following question. In your opinion, is it fair to describe the Mexican-American War as a war of conquest?

West into the Pacific

Graphic Note Taking: Timeline

In the years that followed the Mexican-American War, the Pacific took an increasingly important place in the minds of American policy makers. Manifest Destiny, which began with a vision of North American dominance, expanded to include the Pacific and the projection of American power into East Asia. As you read the section, create a timeline of the key events of U.S. expansion in California and the Pacific Ocean. You'll use your timeline to answer a question when you finish this section.

Reviewing the Facts

Provide a short answer (3-4 sentences) for each of the questions below. It's OK if you need to go back and re-read parts of the section in order to find the answers. The purpose of these questions is not to test you, but to help you discover how much you know and what you might need to review.

1. Why did Catherine Beecher believe it was so important to train young women to become teachers?

2. What were the key components of Horace Mann's program of educational reform?

3. Why were many Roman Catholics hostile to Horace Mann's reforms?

Making Connections

Take another look at the Japanese depiction of Matthew Perry's arrival in Japan on page 341 of your text book. What aspects of Perry's ship and crew did the artist highlight? Why?

Graphic Note Taking: Follow Up

Use your notes to answer the following question. How did the United States become a dominant player in the Pacific in the second half of the nineteenth century?

Fraser: Chapter 12

Complete the following exercises in order *as you read* the chapter.

INTRODUCTION

Introductions provide a valuable guide to the material you are about to read, telling you what topics will be covered and how they fit together. If you keep the "big picture" provided by the introduction in mind as you read the chapter, you'll find it much easier to organize your notes, identify important information, and avoid getting lost in the details. With this in mind, re-read the introduction to Chapter 12. As you read, make a list of the key topics you expect to learn about.

Key Topics

Key Terms

When you finish reading the chapter, identify and explain the importance of the following terms. Use this list to review your understanding of the chapter.

The Changing Face of the American People in the 1840s and 1850s

Graphic Note Taking: Compare and Contrast

By the end of the 1850s, America was a much more diverse nation than it had been two decades earlier. As you read this section, use a table like the one included below to take notes on the experiences of different groups of new Americans in the 1840s and 1850s. You'll use your table to answer a question when you finish this section.

Chinese	Irish	Germans	Mexicans

Reviewing the Facts

Provide a short answer (3-4 sentences) for each of the questions below. It's OK if you need to go back and re-read parts of the section in order to find the answers. The purpose of these questions is not to test you, but to help you discover how much you know and what you might need to review.

1. Why did Chinese migrants come to the United States in large numbers in the 1840s and 1850s?

2. What was the immediate cause of the Great Famine of 1845-1850 in Ireland?

3. What was the United States Land Commission, and what were the consequences of its work?

Making Connections

Take another look at the photograph of California miners on page 353 of your text book. How was life in the gold fields shaped by racial tensions?

Graphic Note Taking: Follow Up

Use your notes to help answer the following question. What role did hard times in China, Ireland, and Germany play in stimulating immigration to the United States in the 1840s and 1850s?

Slavery in the United States, 1840s and 1850s

Graphic Note Taking: Outline

In the second half of the nineteenth century, at the same time that slavery was dying out in the North, slavery grew even more profitable and important in the South. These parallel and divergent developments would have a profound effect on American politics. As you read the section, create an outline like the one included below to help you identify the most important changes in the nature of American slavery in the 1840s and 1850s. You'll use your outline to answer a question when you finish this section.

I. Slavery in the United States, 1840s and 1850s

    A. Slaves and Slave Masters

        1. Rising cotton prices led to a shift of slaves from the coast to new cotton lands

        2. At the same time, northern public opinion was turning against slavery

        3. In response, southerners crafted new arguments in favor of slavery

Reviewing the Facts

Provide a short answer (3-4 sentences) for each of the questions below. It's OK if you need to go back and re-read parts of the section in order to find the answers. The purpose of these questions is not to test you, but to help you discover how much you know and what you might need to review.

1. How did northern public opinion about slavery change after 1830?

2. How did enslaved people resist their enslavement?

3. What methods did William Lloyd Garrison endorse in the struggle to end slavery?

Making Connections

Take another look at the pro-slavery cartoon on page 360 of your text book. What lesson might the artist have intended viewers to take from this work?

Graphic Note Taking: Follow Up

Use your notes to answer the following question. What connections can you make between changes in American slavery and developments in the global economy in the 1840s and 1850s?

New Strengths for American Women

Graphic Note Taking: Identifying Key Figures

At the same time that the anti-slavery movement gained momentum, a number of women, many of them abolitionists, decided the time had come to fight for women's rights. As you read the section, identify the key figures in the early women's rights movement in a list like that included below. Be sure to note the importance of each figure you identify to the cause. You'll use your list to help you answer a question when you finish this section.

[Student answers will vary. Sample entries are included in the list below.]

1. Sarah and Angelina Grimké: [Born into South Carolina slaveholding family, became ardent abolitionists and women's rights advocates, published calls for women's rights]

2. Elizabeth Cady Stanton

3. Lucretia Mott

4.

Reviewing the Facts

Provide a short answer (3-4 sentences) for each of the questions below. It's OK if you need to go back and re-read parts of the section in order to find the answers. The purpose of these questions is not to test you, but to help you discover how much you know and what you might need to review.

1. Why did Sarah Grimké publish her Letters on the *Equality of the Sexes*?

2. How did members of the larger abolitionist movement respond to the Seneca Falls Convention?

3. How did members of the women's rights movement view the issues of marriage and divorce?

Making Connections

Take another look at the illustration of a new women's fashion on page 373 of your text book. What larger cultural trends did this new fashion reflect?

Graphic Note Taking: Follow Up

Use your notes to answer the following question. How did the women's rights movement of the 1840s differ from earlier efforts to call attention to gender-based inequality?

Fraser: Chapter 13

Complete the following exercises in order *as you read* the chapter.

INTRODUCTION

Introductions provide a valuable guide to the material you are about to read, telling you what topics will be covered and how they fit together. If you keep the "big picture" provided by the introduction in mind as you read the chapter, you'll find it much easier to organize your notes, identify important information, and avoid getting lost in the details. With this in mind, re-read the introduction to Chapter 13. As you read, make a list of the key topics you expect to learn about.

Key Topics

Key Terms

When you finish reading the chapter, identify and explain the importance of the following terms. Use this list to review your understanding of the chapter.

From Union to Disunion

Graphic Note Taking: Identify Key Events

By 1850, tensions over the issue of slavery had been building up for decades. Those tensions exploded in 1850 in the debate over the territory acquired in the Mexican-American War and would define the politics of the decade to come. As you read this section, make a list of the key events of the 1850s that moved the nation ever closer to civil war. Make sure to note the importance of each event you include in your list. You'll use your list to answer a question when you finish this section.

[Student answers will vary. Sample entries are included in the table below.]

1.

2.

3.

4.

5.

Reviewing the Facts

Provide a short answer (3-4 sentences) for each of the questions below. It's OK if you need to go back and re-read parts of the section in order to find the answers. The purpose of these questions is not to test you, but to help you discover how much you know and what you might need to review.

1. What were key provisions of the Compromise of 1850?

2. Why was the Fugitive Slave Act of 1850 so much more divisive than previous fugitive slave acts?

3. How did the Republican Party differ from the Whig and Democratic Parties?

Making Connections

Take another look at the poster advertising *Uncle Tom's Cabin* on page 388 of your text book. Why did northerners find the book so compelling? Why did southerners find it so repellent?

Graphic Note Taking: Follow Up

Use your notes to help answer the following question. Why did the Kansas-Nebraska Act prove so

Bleeding Kansas and *Dred Scott v. Sandford*

Graphic Note Taking: Outline

Stephan Douglas hoped that the implementation of "popular sovereignty" would quiet tensions over slavery. It had just the opposite effect, sparking a violent preview of the Civil War in Kansas. At the same time that Kansas bled, the Supreme Court handed down a decision in *Dred Scott v. Sandford* that made future legislative compromises over slavery virtually impossible. As you read the section, create an outline like the one included below to help you understand how these two major events moved the nation closer to civil war. You'll use your outline to answer a question when you finish this section.

    I.   Bleeding Kansas and *Dred Scott v. Sandford*

        A.   Bleeding Kansas

             1.   No one was sure how Kansas and Nebraska would vote on slavery, but many wanted to control the outcome.

             2.   Partisans on both sides of the slavery issue poured into Kansas.

             3.   The first elections returned pro-slavery majorities, but they were marred by cheating, fraudulent vote counting, and voter intimidation.

Reviewing the Facts

Provide a short answer (3-4 sentences) for each of the questions below. It's OK if you need to go back and re-read parts of the section in order to find the answers. The purpose of these questions is not to test you, but to help you discover how much you know and what you might need to review.

1. What impact did Bleeding Kansas have on public opinion?

2. On what basis did Dred Scott claim that he was a free man?

3. What were the key points of the Supreme Court ruling in the *Dred Scott* case?

Making Connections

Take another look at the illustration of the attack by Preston Brooks on Charles Sumner on page 394 of your text book. How did the illustration reflect northern views of southern society and culture?

Graphic Note Taking: Follow Up

Use your notes to answer the following question. How did the Supreme Court's ruling in *Dred Scott v. Sandford* make a civil war more likely?

The Economy, the Panic of 1857, and the Lincoln-Douglas Debates

Graphic Note Taking: Cause and Effect

The debate over slavery was a central cause of the Civil War, but it was not the only development that contributed to the dissolving of the Union. Economic factors were also important. As you read the section, take notes on the key economic developments of the first half of the nineteenth century in table like the one included below. You'll use your table to help you answer a question when you finish this section.

Economic Factor or Development	Consequences

Reviewing the Facts

Provide a short answer (3-4 sentences) for each of the questions below. It's OK if you need to go back and re-read parts of the section in order to find the answers. The purpose of these questions is not to test you, but to help you discover how much you know and what you might need to review.

1. Why did the southern planter elite reject the economic initiatives like import tariffs and infrastructure improvements favored by most northerners?

2. How did Lincoln characterize his position on slavery and race relations during the Lincoln-Douglas debates?

3. How did southerners respond to northern sympathy for John Brown?

Making Connections

Take another look at the painting of John Brown on page 395 of your text book. How did the painting capture northern anti-slavery sentiment?

Graphic Note Taking: Follow Up

Use your notes to answer the following question. How did economic developments divide the nation in the second half of the nineteenth century?

The Election of 1860 and the Secession of the South

Graphic Note Taking: Cause and Effect

The election of 1860 reflected the fact that the time for compromise on slavery had passed. The nation was as politically divided as it had ever been, and neither pro- nor anti-slavery forces were prepared to accept the legitimacy of the election if their chosen candidate was defeated. Consequently, many in the South interpreted Lincoln's victory as clear evidence that they could no longer remain part of the Union. As you read the section, create an outline like the one included below to help you trace the events that led to the outbreak of the Civil War. You'll use your outline to answer a question when you finish this section.

I. The Election of 1860 and the Secession of the South

    A. The Election of Abraham Lincoln

        1. Lincoln was not the frontrunner at the 1860 Republican convention, but skillful management delivered the nomination.

        2. The Republicans emerged as the only truly united party as the election began.

        3. Democrats split over the issue of popular sovereignty.

Reviewing the Facts

Provide a short answer (3-4 sentences) for each of the questions below. It's OK if you need to go back and re-read parts of the section in order to find the answers. The purpose of these questions is not to test you, but to help you discover how much you know and what you might need to review.

1. Why did the Democrats splinter in the run-up to the 1860 election?

2. What was the Crittenden Compromise and why did Lincoln reject it?

3. What kind of a war did most Americans anticipate in the immediate aftermath of the attack on Fort Sumter?

Making Connections

Take another look at Map 13-2: The Election of 1860 on page 399 of your text book. How would you explain Douglas's poor electoral showing?

Graphic Note Taking: Follow Up

Use your notes to answer the following question. In your opinion, why did it prove impossible to hold the Union together after Lincoln was elected president?

Fraser: Chapter 14

Complete the following exercises in order *as you read* the chapter.

INTRODUCTION

Introductions provide a valuable guide to the material you are about to read, telling you what topics will be covered and how they fit together. If you keep the "big picture" provided by the introduction in mind as you read the chapter, you'll find it much easier to organize your notes, identify important information, and avoid getting lost in the details. With this in mind, re-read the introduction to Chapter 14. As you read, make a list of the key topics you expect to learn about.

Key Topics

Key Terms

When you finish reading the chapter, identify and explain the importance of the following terms. Use this list to review your understanding of the chapter.

Fort Sumter to Antietam, 1861-1862

Graphic Note Taking: Compare and Contrast

When war broke out in 1861, neither side was prepared for the drawn-out, bloody conflict to come. Both sides anticipated a short war and employed strategies that reflected that assumption. As you read this section, use a table like the one included below to take notes on advantages, disadvantages, and strategies of the Union and the Confederacy at the outset of the war. You'll use your table to answer a question when you finish this section.

	Advantages	Disadvantages	Strategy
Union			
Confederacy			

Reviewing the Facts

Provide a short answer (3-4 sentences) for each of the questions below. It's OK if you need to go back and re-read parts of the section in order to find the answers. The purpose of these questions is not to test you, but to help you discover how much you know and what you might need to review.

1. What did each side need to do to "win" the war?

2. How did Lincoln respond the Union defeat at the First Battle of Bull Run?

3. Why did many in the South believe that Britain would support their cause? Why did Britain remain neutral?

Making Connections

Take another look at the photograph of the iron clad ship on page 412 of your text book. What role did such vessels play in the Civil War?

Graphic Note Taking: Follow Up

Use your notes to help answer the following question. What was the military situation at the end of 1862?

The Road to Emancipation

Graphic Note Taking: Outline

In 1861, the Civil War was a war to save the Union. On January 1, 1863, it became a war to end slavery. As you read the section, create an outline like the one included below to help you trace the evolution of Union war aims. You'll use your outline to answer a question when you finish this section.

I. The Road to Emancipation

    A. Lincoln's Initial Position

        1. Lincoln claimed that the national government could not interfere with slavery where it existed

        2. After secession, Lincoln's top priority was holding the Union together

        3. Lincoln insisted that his personal dislike of slavery was separate from his duty as president

Reviewing the Facts

Provide a short answer (3-4 sentences) for each of the questions below. It's OK if you need to go back and re-read parts of the section in order to find the answers. The purpose of these questions is not to test you, but to help you discover how much you know and what you might need to review.

1. Why were escaped slaves initially classified as "contraband of war"?

2. What were the limits of the Emancipation Proclamation? What did it accomplish, despite these limits?

3. How did white southerners respond to the increasing presence of African-Americans in the Union army from 1863 on?

Making Connections

Take another look at the photograph of former slaves on page 415 of your text book. Why did the Union have so much difficulty deciding what to do with escaped slaves in the early years of the war?

Graphic Note Taking: Follow Up

Use your notes to answer the following question. How did African-Americans, in both the North and the South, respond to the issuing of the Emancipation Proclamation?

The Home Front – Shortages, Opposition, Riots, and Battles

Graphic Note Taking: Compare and Contrast

As the war dragged on, its effects on the home front intensified. More and more families were touched by the death and destruction of the battlefield and shortages made life hard for many. As you read the section, use a table like the one included below to take notes on the impact of the war on the home front in the North and in the South. You'll use your table to help you answer a question when you finish this section.

North	South

Reviewing the Facts

Provide a short answer (3-4 sentences) for each of the questions below. It's OK if you need to go back and re-read parts of the section in order to find the answers. The purpose of these questions is not to test you, but to help you discover how much you know and what you might need to review.

1. Why did the Confederacy's efforts to solve its financial problems lead to inflation?

2. Why did managing the home front in the South primarily fall to women?

3. What led to the 1863 New York Draft Riot? What groups were the targets of the rioters' anger?

Making Connections

Take another look at the illustration of a bread riot on page 420 of your text book. What should we make of the fact that all of the participants are women?

Graphic Note Taking: Follow Up

Use your notes to answer the following question. Why were wartime conditions in the South so much worse than in the North?

From Gettysburg to Appomattox and Beyond

Graphic Note Taking: Mastering the Details

The Confederacy reached its military high point in June 1863, but Union victories at Gettysburg and Vicksburg in July turned the war decisively in the Union's favor. Nonetheless, it would take two more years of hard fighting to bring the war to an end. As you read the section, make a list of the key battles of the latter part of the war, beginning with Gettysburg and Vicksburg. Be sure to note the importance of each battle you include in your list. You'll use your list to help answer a question when you have finished with this section.

1. Gettysburg

2. Vicksburg

3.

4.

5.

Reviewing the Facts

Provide a short answer (3-4 sentences) for each of the questions below. It's OK if you need to go back and re-read parts of the section in order to find the answers. The purpose of these questions is not to test you, but to help you discover how much you know and what you might need to review.

1. Why did the Civil War's death toll escalate in the last years of the war?

2. What connection was there between events at Petersburg and presidential politics in the North in 1864? How does this connection help explain Lee's determination to hold on to Petersburg?

3. What contentious political issues did the country face in the aftermath of Union victory and the abolition of slavery?

Making Connections

Take another look at the photograph of Clara Barton on page 427 of your text book. What role did women like Barton play in the war effort?

Graphic Note Taking: Follow Up

Use your notes to answer the following question. Why were the Union victories at Gettysburg and Vicksburg so important?

Fraser: Chapter 15

Complete the following exercises in order *as you read* the chapter.

INTRODUCTION

Introductions provide a valuable guide to the material you are about to read, telling you what topics will be covered and how they fit together. If you keep the "big picture" provided by the introduction in mind as you read the chapter, you'll find it much easier to organize your notes, identify important information, and avoid getting lost in the details. With this in mind, re-read the introduction to Chapter 15. As you read, make a list of the key topics you expect to learn about.

Key Topics

Key Terms

When you finish reading the chapter, identify and explain the importance of the following terms. Use this list to review your understanding of the chapter.

Federal Reconstruction Strategy

Graphic Note Taking: Compare and Contrast

With the war over, attention soon turned to the terms under which southern states would be readmitted to the Union. President Johnson shaped and implemented the first efforts in this context, but Republican anger with Johnson's limited vision of Reconstruction led to impeachment proceedings and congressional control of the process. As you read this section, use a table like the one included below to take notes the differences between Congressional and Presidential Reconstruction. You'll use your table to answer a question when you finish this section.

	Policies	Goals
Presidential Reconstruction		
Congressional Reconstruction		

Reviewing the Facts

Provide a short answer (3-4 sentences) for each of the questions below. It's OK if you need to go back and re-read parts of the section in order to find the answers. The purpose of these questions is not to test you, but to help you discover how much you know and what you might need to review.

1. What were the key elements of Johnson's plans for Reconstruction?

2. Why was Johnson so determined to fight against equal rights for blacks?

3. What were the key provisions of the Reconstruction Act of 1867?

Making Connections

Take another look at the illustration of the Freedmen's Bureau in action on page 443 of your text book. What role did the Freedmen's Bureau play in the post-war South?

Graphic Note Taking: Follow Up

Use your notes to help answer the following question. How did Jackson's actions and policies broaden congressional support for "Radical Reconstruction"?

The Impact of Reconstruction

Graphic Note Taking: Identifying Key Developments

While debate raged in Washington about the status of newly freed slaves, the former slaves themselves were clear about what they wanted and how they expected to be treated. As you read this section, use a table like the one included below to take notes on the priorities and expectations of the freedmen. You'll use your table to answer a question when you finish this section.

Political and Civil Rights	Education	Land and Economic Opportunity

Reviewing the Facts

Provide a short answer (3-4 sentences) for each of the questions below. It's OK if you need to go back and re-read parts of the section in order to find the answers. The purpose of these questions is not to test you, but to help you discover how much you know and what you might need to review.

1. What were the most significant accomplishments of Reconstruction state governments?

2. How did the Reconstruction Act of 1867 shape late nineteenth-century education in the South?

3. Why did so many former slaves reject the idea of working for whites for wages? What kind of economic opportunity did they want instead?

Making Connections

Take another look at the drawing of a school operated by the Freedmen's Bureau on page 456 of your text book. Who are the teachers? Where did they likely come from?

Graphic Note Taking: Follow Up

Use your notes to answer the following question. How did former slaves define freedom, and what did they think was required to turn the promise of freedom into a reality?

Terror, Apathy, and the Creation of the Segregated South

Graphic Note Taking: Timeline

By the end of the 1860s, southern whites were engaged in an all-out war against Reconstruction, determined to return to the pre-war political and racial status quo by any means necessary. As you read the section, create a timeline tracing the escalation of political violence in the South, as well as the response of northern officials to that violence. You'll use your timeline to help you answer a question when you have finished with this section.

Reviewing the Facts

Provide a short answer (3-4 sentences) for each of the questions below. It's OK if you need to go back and re-read parts of the section in order to find the answers. The purpose of these questions is not to test you, but to help you discover how much you know and what you might need to review.

1. What were the key goals and characteristics of the post-war Democratic Party in the South?

2. What steps did the federal government take to defend Reconstruction from Democratic "redeemers"?

3. What forms of segregation emerged in the South after 1877? How was segregation enforced?

Making Connections

Take another look at the illustration of two Klan members on page 463 of your text book. What were the Klan's goals?

Graphic Note Taking: Follow Up

Use your notes to answer the following question. In your opinion, is it fair to describe the political violence that accompanied Redemption as "terrorism"? Why or why not?

Fraser: Chapter 16

Complete the following exercises in order *as you read* the chapter.

INTRODUCTION

Introductions provide a valuable guide to the material you are about to read, telling you what topics will be covered and how they fit together. If you keep the "big picture" provided by the introduction in mind as you read the chapter, you'll find it much easier to organize your notes, identify important information, and avoid getting lost in the details. With this in mind, re-read the introduction to Chapter 16. As you read, make a list of the key topics you expect to learn about.

Key Topics

Key Terms

When you finish reading the chapter, identify and explain the importance of the following terms. Use this list to review your understanding of the chapter.

The Tribes of the West and the U.S. Government

Graphic Note Taking: Compare and Contrast

Once the Civil War was over, the government gave renewed attention to Indian peoples, particularly those of the Great Plains. Westward migration of whites resumed and conflicts between whites and Indians intensified. As you read this section, use a table like the one included below to take notes on the impact of these developments for major Indian groups. You'll use your table to answer a question when you finish this section.

	General Characteristics in Post-Civil War Period	Interactions with U.S. Government
The Comanche Empire		
The Navajos and Apaches		
The Medocs, the Nez Perce, and the Pacific Coast Tribes		
The Lakota Sioux		

Reviewing the Facts

Provide a short answer (3-4 sentences) for each of the questions below. It's OK if you need to go back and re-read parts of the section in order to find the answers. The purpose of these questions is not to test you, but to help you discover how much you know and what you might need to review.

1. How did the U.S. government interpret the Medicine Lodge Creek Treaty? How did the Comanche

2. What factors combined to make the Bosque Redondo a complete failure?

3. What considerations shaped Ulysses S. Grant's Peace Policy?

Making Connections

Take another look at the photograph of the Ghost Dance on page 487 of your text book. What did the dance mean to the Indians who participated in it? What did it mean to whites who witnessed it?

Graphic Note Taking: Follow Up

Use your notes to help answer the following question. How did various Indian groups respond to efforts to force them onto reservations in the decades following the Civil War?

The Impact of the Transcontinental Railroad, 1869

Graphic Note Taking: Outline

The construction of a transcontinental railroad was one of the most important American engineering feats of the nineteenth century. As you read the section, create an outline like the one included below to help you identify the most important consequences of the completion of the transcontinental railroad. You'll use your outline to answer a question when you finish this section.

    I.   The Impact of the Transcontinental Railroad

        A. Building the Transcontinental Railroad

            1.   Before the Civil War, a variety of routes were proposed for the railroad.

            2.   After the war began, a northerly route was chosen and work began in 1862.

            3.   The end of the war brought a rush to complete construction

Reviewing the Facts

Provide a short answer (3-4 sentences) for each of the questions below. It's OK if you need to go back and re-read parts of the section in order to find the answers. The purpose of these questions is not to test you, but to help you discover how much you know and what you might need to review.

1. What roles were played by the Central Pacific railroad, the Union Pacific railroad, and the federal government in the construction of the transcontinental railroad?

2. How did technological innovations contribute to the growth of the nation's railroad network in the post-Civil War era?

3. Why did trains lead many Americans to develop a new sense of time?

Making Connections

Take another look at the photograph of Chinese railroad workers on page 491 of your text book. What challenges and obstacles did construction of the transcontinental railroad present?

Graphic Note Taking: Follow Up

Use your notes to answer the following question. What were the most important economic consequences of the expansion of the nation's railroad network in the decades following the Civil War?

The Transformation of the West

Graphic Note Taking: Cause and Effect

Railroads, the defeat of the Indians, and a new wave of white settlement combined to transform the West. As you read this section, use a table like the one included below to take notes on the changing social, political, and economic order in the West in the late nineteenth century. You'll use your table to answer a question when you finish this section.

Western Society
The Western Economy
Western Politics

Reviewing the Facts

Provide a short answer (3-4 sentences) for each of the questions below. It's OK if you need to go back and re-read parts of the section in order to find the answers. The purpose of these questions is not to test you, but to help you discover how much you know and what you might need to review.

1. What led to the post-Civil War cattle boom?

2. How and why did Latino resistance in New Mexico and Texas differ?

3. What were the consequences for Indians and Latinos of the influx of white settlers, particularly farmers, after 1870?

Making Connections

Take another look at the photograph of a Colorado mining town on page 503 of your text book. How did

Graphic Note Taking: Follow Up

Use your notes to answer the following question. In your opinion, does the term "Wild West" create a fair and accurate impression of the late nineteenth-century American West? Why or why not?

Fraser: Chapter 17

Complete the following exercises in order *as you read* the chapter.

INTRODUCTION

Introductions provide a valuable guide to the material you are about to read, telling you what topics will be covered and how they fit together. If you keep the "big picture" provided by the introduction in mind as you read the chapter, you'll find it much easier to organize your notes, identify important information, and avoid getting lost in the details. With this in mind, re-read the introduction to Chapter 17. As you read, make a list of the key topics you expect to learn about.

Key Topics

Key Terms

When you finish reading the chapter, identify and explain the importance of the following terms. Use this list to review your understanding of the chapter.

Technology Changes the Nation

Graphic Note Taking: Mastering the Details

The late nineteenth century saw an unprecedented burst of technological innovation. Collectively, the new inventions transformed American life. As you read this section, make a list of the most important inventions of the era. Be sure to note the importance of each invention you include. You'll use your list to answer a question when you finish this section.

Invention	Importance
1.	
2.	
3.	
4.	
5.	
6.	

Reviewing the Facts

Provide a short answer (3-4 sentences) for each of the questions below. It's OK if you need to go back and re-read parts of the section in order to find the answers. The purpose of these questions is not to test you, but to help you discover how much you know and what you might need to review.

1. How quickly was the telephone adopted by American consumers following its patent in 1876? What does the rate of adoption suggest about American society in the late nineteenth century?

2. How did Edison fund his research into electric lights and, once invented, how did he publicize his electric light bulb?

3. What was Henry Ford's key contribution to the automobile industry?

Making Connections

Take another look at Table 17-1: Factory Sales of Passenger Cars per Year on page 512 of your text book. What important patterns do you see in the data the table presents?

Graphic Note Taking: Follow Up

Use your notes to help answer the following question. Why did the advent of inexpensive automobiles have such a profound impact on American society and the American economy?

Corporations and Monopolies

Graphic Note Taking: Outline

The changing economic environment of the late nineteenth century required new business models. The translation of the new inventions of the era into new industries required enormous investments in money and manpower. As banks and corporations grew in response to post-Civil War challenges and opportunities, a tiny group of Americans became richer and more powerful than any Americans before them. As you read the section, create an outline like the one included below to help you trace the development of American big business. You'll use your outline to answer a question when you finish this section.

    I.   The Panic of 1873

        A. Jay Cooke

            1.   Most powerful banker in U.S. in 1865

            2.   Financed the Northern Pacific Railroad

            3.   Overproduction and overseas developments led to bankruptcy

Reviewing the Facts

Provide a short answer (3-4 sentences) for each of the questions below. It's OK if you need to go back and re-read parts of the section in order to find the answers. The purpose of these questions is not to test you, but to help you discover how much you know and what you might need to review.

1. What led to the Panic of 1893 and the depression that followed?

2. How did Standard Oil achieve a near monopoly of the oil refining industry?

3. How did the structure and organization of Carnegie Steel differ from that of Standard Oil?

Making Connections

Take another look at the photograph of George Vanderbilt's estate on page 515 of your text book. What sort of statement might Vanderbilt have been trying to make with this grand mansion?

Graphic Note Taking: Follow Up

Use your notes to answer the following question. How did the industrial and financial leaders of the Gilded Age increase and consolidate their wealth and power?

The Lives of the Middle Class in the Gilded Age

Graphic Note Taking: Charting the Growing Influence of the Middle Class

The new middle class that emerged in the late nineteenth century had a far-reaching impact on American life, influencing the values that were seen as quintessentially American, the nature and design of American cities, the issues that dominated national politics, and the foreign policy pursued by the American government. As you read this section, use a table like the one included below to take notes on the impact of the new middle class. You'll use your table to answer a question when you finish this section.

Values:

Cities:

Politics:

Foreign Policy:

Reviewing the Facts

Provide a short answer (3-4 sentences) for each of the questions below. It's OK if you need to go back and re-read parts of the section in order to find the answers. The purpose of these questions is not to test you, but to help you discover how much you know and what you might need to review.

1. Why did late nineteenth-century cities focus their resources on improving the quality of their water supply?

2. How did the new middle class shape the electoral politics of the late nineteenth century?

3. Why did the pace of American overseas economic expansion quicken after the Panic of 1873?

Making Connections

Take another look at the painting of New York at night on page 522 of your text book. How did the technological innovations depicted in the painting make the emergence of the new middle class possible?

Graphic Note Taking: Follow Up

Use your notes to answer the following question. Who belonged to the new middle class and what values and priorities did that class promote?

Immigration

Graphic Note Taking: Cause and Effect

The United States experienced a surge of new immigration in the late nineteenth century. Immigrants came from many countries, pushed by conditions at home and pulled by the promise of a better life in the United States. As you read this section, use a table like the one included below to identify the push and pull factors that brought different groups of immigrants to the United States. You'll use your table to answer a question when you finish this section.

	Push Factors	Pull Factors
Russian and Eastern European Jews		
Southern Italians		
Chinese		

Reviewing the Facts

Provide a short answer (3-4 sentences) for each of the questions below. It's OK if you need to go back and re-read parts of the section in order to find the answers. The purpose of these questions is not to test you, but to help you discover how much you know and what you might need to review.

1. How did immigration patterns between 1815 and 1890 differ from immigration patterns between 1890 and 1914?

2. How did Russian government policies stimulate Jewish emigration?

3. What was the experience of Ellis Island like for most immigrants?

Making Connections

Take another look at the photograph of Japanese immigrants at Angel Island on page 532 of your text book. What similarities and differences were there in the experiences of Asian and European immigrants?

Graphic Note Taking: Follow Up

Use your notes to answer the following question. Why were Russian and eastern European Jewish immigrants among the least likely immigrants to return to their home countries?

Fraser: Chapter 18

Complete the following exercises in order *as you read* the chapter.

INTRODUCTION

Introductions provide a valuable guide to the material you are about to read, telling you what topics will be covered and how they fit together. If you keep the "big picture" provided by the introduction in mind as you read the chapter, you'll find it much easier to organize your notes, identify important information, and avoid getting lost in the details. With this in mind, re-read the introduction to Chapter 18. As you read, make a list of the key topics you expect to learn about.

Key Topics

Key Terms

When you finish reading the chapter, identify and explain the importance of the following terms. Use this list to review your understanding of the chapter.

Conflict in the New South

Graphic Note Taking: Outline

In the 1880s, some in the South believed it was time for the region to enter a new era. In their view, a New South was being born, one which was unapologetic about the past and optimistic about the future. At the same time, however, many southerners, especially African Americans, were left out of the prosperity the New South promised. As you read the section, create an outline like the one included below to help you trace developments in the South in the late nineteenth century. You'll use your outline to answer a question when you finish this section.

    I.   The New South

          A.   Economic Development

                    1.   Prior to the Civil War, South had far fewer miles of railroad track than North

                    2.   Railroad boom provided jobs and created new social and economic connections

                    3.   New industries helped diversify the southern economy

Reviewing the Facts

Provide a short answer (3-4 sentences) for each of the questions below. It's OK if you need to go back and re-read parts of the section in order to find the answers. The purpose of these questions is not to test you, but to help you discover how much you know and what you might need to review.

1. How did the railroad boom of the late nineteenth century affect the South?

2. What impact did the new state constitutions of the 1890s have on southern blacks?

3. How did Booker T. Washington propose that blacks respond to the challenges posed by segregation and discrimination?

Making Connections

Take another look at the photograph of a southern parade float on page 542 of your text book. What might explain the nostalgia many late nineteenth-century southern whites felt for the Old South?

Graphic Note Taking: Follow Up

Use your notes to answer the following question. What was new about the New South? In what ways was the New South very much like the Old South?

The Politics of Conflict – From Populist Movement to Populist Party

Graphic Note Taking: Mastering the Details

The 1870s and 1880s were difficult times for American farmers. Increasingly vulnerable to global economic developments and business cycles, farmers organized to increase their economic power and to gain a political voice. As you read the section, create a list of important farmers' organizations, noting the membership and agenda of each organization you include. You'll use your list to answer a question when you finish this section.

1.

2.

3.

4.

5.

Reviewing the Facts

Provide a short answer (3-4 sentences) for each of the questions below. It's OK if you need to go back and re-read parts of the section in order to find the answers. The purpose of these questions is not to test you, but to help you discover how much you know and what you might need to review.

1. What kinds of economic problems did farmers face in the late nineteenth century?

2. What were the main objectives of the Farmers' Alliance under the leadership of Henry Macune?

3. Why was government policy regarding the money supply such a vital issue for farmers in the late nineteenth century?

Making Connections

Take another look at the Grange poster on page 549 of your text book. What values did the poster celebrate?

Graphic Note Taking: Follow Up

Use your notes to answer the following question. What issues were most important to farmers in the

Workers Protest and the Rise of Organized Labor

Graphic Note Taking: Compare and Contrast

At the same time that farmers were organizing to advance their shared interests, other kinds of workers were creating organizations designed to give them a collective voice. As you read this section, use a table like the one included below to compare and contrast three important labor organizations: the Knights of Labor, the American Federation of Labor, and the International Workers of the World. You'll use your table to answer a question when you finish this section.

[

	Membership	Goals	Achievements
Knights of Labor			
American Federation of Labor			
International Workers of the World			

Reviewing the Facts

Provide a short answer (3-4 sentences) for each of the questions below. It's OK if you need to go back and re-read parts of the section in order to find the answers. The purpose of these questions is not to test you, but to help you discover how much you know and what you might need to review.

1. What were some of the long-term consequences of the Great Railroad Strike of 1877?

2. What were the goals and principles of the Knights of Labor under Terrance Powderly's leadership?

3. What was the long-term impact of the Haymarket bombing?

Making Connections

Take another look at the image of federal troops escorting a Pullman train on page 560 of your text book. How did the artist see the strike? What role did he or she suggest the government played in ending it?

Graphic Note Taking: Follow Up

Use your notes to answer the following question. What were the most important differences between the Knights of Labor and the American Federation of Labor?

Fraser: Chapter 19

Complete the following exercises in order *as you read* the chapter.

INTRODUCTION

Introductions provide a valuable guide to the material you are about to read, telling you what topics will be covered and how they fit together. If you keep the "big picture" provided by the introduction in mind as you read the chapter, you'll find it much easier to organize your notes, identify important information, and avoid getting lost in the details. With this in mind, re-read the introduction to Chapter 19. As you read, make a list of the key topics you expect to learn about.

Key Topics

Key Terms

When you finish reading the chapter, identify and explain the importance of the following terms. Use this list to review your understanding of the chapter.

The Revolt of the Intellectuals

Graphic Note Taking: Mastering the Details

As the challenges associated with industrialization, urban growth, and immigration intensified, a number of scholars and thinkers began to look for more effective responses. As you read the section, make a list of the most important social and economic theorists discussed in the text. Be sure to note the importance of each individual you include. You'll use your list to help you answer a question when you finish the section.

1.

2.

3.

4.

5.

Reviewing the Facts

Provide a short answer (3-4 sentences) for each of the questions below. It's OK if you need to go back and re-read parts of the section in order to find the answers. The purpose of these questions is not to test you, but to help you discover how much you know and what you might need to review.

1. What solution did Henry George offer to the country's economic and social problems?

2. How did William Graham Sumner apply Darwin's biological theories to social issues?

3. What basic ideas did John Dewey, Richard Ely, and Albion Small have in common?

Making Connections

Take another look at the image of a meat-packing plant on page 571 of your text book. What clues does the image offer that this plant is operating in a way that is consistent with progressive standards?

Graphic Note Taking: Follow Up

Use your notes to answer the following question. How did scholars like John Dewey and Richard Ely challenge the social and economic status quo?

The Transformation of the Cities

Graphic Note Taking: Compare and Contrast

At the epicenter of many of the most important social and economic changes of the late nineteenth century, cities were a major focus of progressive activism. In their efforts to promote urban reform, progressives often found themselves at odds with existing political machines. As you read the section, use the table included below to compare and contrast the approach of political machines and progressives to the challenges of urban government. You'll use your table to answer a question when you finish this section.

Political Machines	Progressives

Reviewing the Facts

Provide a short answer (3-4 sentences) for each of the questions below. It's OK if you need to go back and re-read parts of the section in order to find the answers. The purpose of these questions is not to test you, but to help you discover how much you know and what you might need to review.

1. How did political bosses like William Tweed secure the political loyalty of poor urban voters?

2. Why did some urban residents, particularly poor immigrants, resent progressive efforts at urban reform?

3. How did initiative, referendum, and recall measures increase the direct participation of voters in government?

Making Connections

Take another look at the cartoon of a party boss on page 573 of your text book. What message was the cartoon meant to convey about machine government?

Graphic Note Taking: Follow Up

Use your notes to answer the following question. In your opinion, was the progressive critique of political machines justified? Why or why not?

Religious Responses to the Gilded Age

Graphic Note Taking: Outline

In the late 1800s, there were often close ties between social reform movements and religious revivals. As you read the section, create an outline like the one included below to help you trace the connections between revival and reform. You'll use your outline to answer a question when you finish this section.

I. Religious Responses to the Gilded Age

    A. Temperance and the Women's Christian Temperance Union

        1. New temperance movement rooted in Protestant revival

        2. Panic of 1872 sparked new movement

        3. Most early leaders were women

Reviewing the Facts

Provide a short answer (3-4 sentences) for each of the questions below. It's OK if you need to go back and re-read parts of the section in order to find the answers. The purpose of these questions is not to test you, but to help you discover how much you know and what you might need to review.

1. What connection did Frances Willard make between temperance and women's suffrage?

2. What did the temperance movement suggest about the power of organized religion, particularly Protestantism, in late nineteenth-century politics?

3. What was the Social Gospel? What kinds of initiatives did its proponents support?

Making Connections

Take another look at Map 19-1: Prohibition in the States on page 580 of your text book. Where did temperance have its earliest success? Why?

Graphic Note Taking: Follow Up

Use your notes to answer the following question. How would you explain the heavy representation of women in the late nineteenth-century temperance movement?

Progressive Politics on the National Stage

Graphic Note Taking: Compare and Contrast

The elevation of Theodore Roosevelt to the presidency in 1900 marked the beginning of two decades of progressive prominence in national politics. As you read the section, create a table like the one included below to help you compare and contrast the accomplishments of three progressive presidents: Theodore Roosevelt, William Taft, and Woodrow Wilson. You'll use your table to help you answer a question when you finish the section.

Theodore Roosevelt	William Taft	Woodrow Wilson

Reviewing the Facts

Provide a short answer (3-4 sentences) for each of the questions below. It's OK if you need to go back and re-read parts of the section in order to find the answers. The purpose of these questions is not to test you, but to help you discover how much you know and what you might need to review.

1. What new tools did Roosevelt want to control large companies? What did he do with them once he got them?

2. In what areas did Taft prove to be a more vigorous progressive than Roosevelt?

3. Despite his accomplishments, what supporters were most disappointed with Wilson's performance in office?

Making Connections

Take another look at the photograph of Theodore Roosevelt on page 585 of your text book. What qualities might the photographer have wanted the viewer to associate with Roosevelt?

Graphic Note Taking: Follow Up

Use your notes to answer the following question. In your opinion, which of these three presidents was most successful at advancing the progressive agenda? Why?

Fraser: Chapter 20

Complete the following exercises in order *as you read* the chapter.

INTRODUCTION

Introductions provide a valuable guide to the material you are about to read, telling you what topics will be covered and how they fit together. If you keep the "big picture" provided by the introduction in mind as you read the chapter, you'll find it much easier to organize your notes, identify important information, and avoid getting lost in the details. With this in mind, re-read the introduction to Chapter 20. As you read, make a list of the key topics you expect to learn about.

Key Topics

Key Terms

When you finish reading the chapter, identify and explain the importance of the following terms. Use this list to review your understanding of the chapter.

Continuing Expansion

Graphic Note Taking: Compare and Contrast

American expansion continued unabated throughout the Progressive Era. At the turn of the century, many American policy makers believed control of the Pacific was key to the nation's continued growth. With that in mind, they concentrated on acquiring territory that would help the United States achieve that goal. As you read the section, create a table like the one included below to compare and contrast the acquisitions of Alaska and Hawaii. You'll use your table to help you answer a question when you finish the section.

	Alaska	Hawaii
Method of Acquisition		
Justification for Acquisition		
Public Response to Acquisition		

Reviewing the Facts

Provide a short answer (3-4 sentences) for each of the questions below. It's OK if you need to go back and re-read parts of the section in order to find the answers. The purpose of these questions is not to test you, but to help you discover how much you know and what you might need to review.

1. What did Alfred Mahan argue in *The Influence of Sea Power upon History* and how did his book influence the course of American foreign policy?

2. Why was the Russian government willing to part with Alaska?

3. Why did U.S. interest in Hawaii intensify in the second half of the nineteenth century?

Making Connections

Take another look at Map 20-1: The U.S. in the World, 1900 on page 605 of your text book. How would you explain the evident American interest in Pacific islands during the nineteenth century?

Graphic Note Taking: Follow Up

Use your notes to answer the following question. What similarities and differences were there in the acquisition of Alaska and Hawaii? How would you explain the differences you note?

The Splendid Little War...with Spain, Cuba, Puerto Rico, and the Philippines, 1898

Graphic Note Taking: Contrasting Opinions

While the Spanish-American War was sparked by events in Cuba, it quickly widened to include other elements of Spain's colonial empire. Once Spain was defeated, President McKinley negotiated the transfer of a number of those colonies, including Puerto Rico and the Philippines, to the United States. As you read the section, use the table below to take notes on the ensuing debate over America's acquisition of overseas colonies. You'll use your table to answer a question when you finish this section.

Arguments in Favor of Overseas Expansion	Arguments Against Overseas Expansion

Reviewing the Facts

Provide a short answer (3-4 sentences) for each of the questions below. It's OK if you need to go back and re-read parts of the section in order to find the answers. The purpose of these questions is not to test you, but to help you discover how much you know and what you might need to review.

1. How did American interest in Cuba evolve over the course of the nineteenth century?

2. What sparked the 1895 Cuban Revolution?

3. Why was the conclusion of the Spanish-American War followed by a new conflict in the Philippines?

Making Connections

Take another look at the photograph of Filipino prisoners on page 606 of your text book. How did American policy makers justify the American occupation and rule of the Philippines?

Graphic Note Taking: Follow Up

Use your table to answer the following question. In your opinion, did the United States become an imperialist power at the turn of the twentieth century? Why or why not?

Foreign Policy, Foreign Adventures, 1900-1914

Graphic Note Taking: Outline

By the early twentieth century, it was clear that the United States had become a major global power. As you read the section, create an outline like the one included below to help you trace the development of American foreign policy in years leading up to World War I. You'll use your outline to answer a question when you finish this section.

I. Foreign Policy, Foreign Adventures, 1900-1914

    A. A Canal in Panama

        1. Many obstacles to construction of a canal

        2. Clayton-Bulwer Treaty (1850) laid groundwork for joint American-British canal

        3. Interest in building a canal intensified at the turn of the century

Reviewing the Facts

Provide a short answer (3-4 sentences) for each of the questions below. It's OK if you need to go back and re-read parts of the section in order to find the answers. The purpose of these questions is not to test you, but to help you discover how much you know and what you might need to review.

1. How did Roosevelt use the financial problems of the Dominican Republic to expand on the Monroe Doctrine?

2. What role did Roosevelt play in ending the Russo-Japanese War?

3. Why did Wilson find it so difficult to avoid intervening in Mexico?

Making Connections

Take another look at Map 20-2: U.S. Intervention in the Caribbean and Latin America on page 614 of your text book. How would you explain the frequent intervention of the United States in the Caribbean and Latin America in the early decades of the twentieth century?

Graphic Note Taking: Follow Up

Use your notes to answer the following question. How did anti-Japanese sentiment in the United States, particularly in California, shape U.S.-Japanese relations?

The United States and the Great War

Graphic Note Taking: Timeline

In 1914, events in Europe sparked a global war. The United States declared neutrality, but that proved to be a difficult position to maintain. As you read this section, create a timeline of events from the start of the war in 1914 to U.S. entry in 1917. You'll use your timeline to help you answer a question when you finish the section.

Reviewing the Facts

Provide a short answer (3-4 sentences) for each of the questions below. It's OK if you need to go back and re-read parts of the section in order to find the answers. The purpose of these questions is not to test you, but to help you discover how much you know and what you might need to review.

1. How did the assassination of Archduke Franz Ferdinand lead to a war involving all of Europe?

2. What steps did the American government take to control public opinion after the United States entered the war?

3. What general goals and principles did Wilson articulate in his Fourteen Points?

Making Connections

Take another look at the anti-war poster on page 617 of your text book. Why did so many Americans opose United States participation in World War I?

Graphic Note Taking: Follow Up

Use your notes to answer the following question. Why, despite President Wilson's strong stand in favor of neutrality, was America unable to stay out of World War I?

Fraser: Chapter 21

Complete the following exercises in order *as you read* the chapter.

INTRODUCTION

Introductions provide a valuable guide to the material you are about to read, telling you what topics will be covered and how they fit together. If you keep the "big picture" provided by the introduction in mind as you read the chapter, you'll find it much easier to organize your notes, identify important information, and avoid getting lost in the details. With this in mind, re-read the introduction to Chapter 21. As you read, make a list of the key topics you expect to learn about.

Key Topics

Key Terms

When you finish reading the chapter, identify and explain the importance of the following terms. Use this list to review your understanding of the chapter.

The Prelude—The Red Summer of 1919

Graphic Note Taking: Cause and Effect

The transition from war to peace was not a smooth one. As the troops returned home, economic problems, labor conflicts, and a wave of anti-radical hysteria gripped the nation. As you read the section, create a table like the one included below to help you identify the key factors contributing to postwar turmoil. Be sure to note the consequences of each factor you identify. You'll use your table to help you answer a question when you finish the section.

Factor	Consequence

Reviewing the Facts

Provide a short answer (3-4 sentences) for each of the questions below. It's OK if you need to go back and re-read parts of the section in order to find the answers. The purpose of these questions is not to test you, but to help you discover how much you know and what you might need to review.

1. What connections did some Americans, including the Attorney General A. Mitchell Palmer, make between labor unrest and the Russian Revolution?

2. Why did anti-radical hysteria subside in 1920?

3. What factors combined to produce the race riots that rocked the country in the summer of 1919?

Making Connections

Take another look at the photograph of the Red Cross Motor Corps on page 635 of your text book. How might the influenza epidemic of 1919 have contributed to the tense postwar mood?

Graphic Note Taking: Follow Up

Use your notes to answer the following question. Why did fears about leftwing political radicalism escalate in the immediate postwar period?

The 1920s – The Exuberance of Prosperity

Graphic Note Taking: Outline

The economic prosperity of the 1920s was accompanied by sometimes unsettling social and cultural change. As you read the section, create an outline like the one included below to help you identify the most important social and cultural trends of the decade. You'll use your outline to help you answer a question when you complete the section.

I.   The 1920s – The Exuberance of Prosperity

    A.   Prohibition – The Campaign for Moral Conformity

        1.   Prohibition, and the resistance to it, defined the 1920s for many

        2.   Prohibition had a long history stretching back to the 1830s

        3.   The Anti-Saloon League led the early twentieth-century prohibition movement

Reviewing the Facts

Provide a short answer (3-4 sentences) for each of the questions below. It's OK if you need to go back and re-read parts of the section in order to find the answers. The purpose of these questions is not to test you, but to help you discover how much you know and what you might need to review.

1. What connections were there between the prohibition movement and anti-immigrant sentiment?

2. How did technological changes in the 1920s reshape the way Americans thought about culture and morality?

3. What factors helped spark the beginning of the Great Migration?

Making Connections

Take another look at the photograph of Marcus Garvey and his followers on page 648 of your text book. How might lavish uniforms and parades have helped to advance Garvey's agenda?

Graphic Note Taking: Follow Up

Use your table to answer the following question. In what ways were gender and sexual norms challenged in the 1920s?

The 1920s – Conflicts About American Ideals

Graphic Note Taking: Charting Parallel Developments

Not everyone participated in or was pleased about the social and cultural changes of the 1920s. Many Americans, particularly rural Americans, believed that the country was moving in the wrong direction and that it was critical that they offer a spirited resistance to change. As you read the section, create a table like the one included below to help you understand three important manifestations of cultural conflict in the 1920s: the Ku Klux Klan, fundamentalism, and the resurgence of anti-immigrant sentiment. You'll use your table to help you answer a question when you finish the section

The New Kan	Fundamentalism	Anti-Immigrant Sentiment

Reviewing the Facts

Provide a short answer (3-4 sentences) for each of the questions below. It's OK if you need to go back and re-read parts of the section in order to find the answers. The purpose of these questions is not to test you, but to help you discover how much you know and what you might need to review.

1. What was the Eugenics Movement and how did it support efforts to limit immigration?

2. Why did the end of World War I produce hardship for rural America?

3. How did the fundamentalist perspective on the United States and its future differ from the more traditional Protestant outlook?

Making Connections

Take another look at the photograph of a Klan rally on page 649 of your text book. How would you explain the Klan's emergence as a mainstream organization in the 1920s?

Graphic Note Taking: Follow Up

Use your notes to answer the following question. What connections can you make between the rise of the new Klan, the passage of immigration restrictions, and the growing appeal of fundamentalist Protestant Christianity?

Harding, Coolidge, and Hoover – National Politics and Policies in the 1920s

Graphic Note Taking: Compare and Contrast

Republicans held the White House throughout the 1920s, setting the national political agenda and directing America's foreign policy. As you read this section, use a table like the once included below to compare and contrast the policies of the three Republican presidents of the 1920s: Warren Harding, Calvin Coolidge, and Herbert Hoover. You'll use your table to help you answer a question when you finish the section.

	Domestic Policy	Foreign Policy
Harding		
Coolidge		
Hoover		

Reviewing the Facts

Provide a short answer (3-4 sentences) for each of the questions below. It's OK if you need to go back and re-read parts of the section in order to find the answers. The purpose of these questions is not to test you, but to help you discover how much you know and what you might need to review.

1. How did the men who Harding appointed to his cabinet help advance the Republican agenda?

2. What explains Coolidge's decisive victory in the 1924 election?

3. Compare and contrast Herbert Hoover and Al Smith. In what ways were their positions similar? What were the most important differences between the two candidates for president in 1928?

Making Connections

Take another look at the political cartoon on page 658 of your text book. How was Coolidge able to avoid paying a political price for the scandals that occurred during the Harding administration?

Graphic Note Taking: Follow Up

Use your notes to answer the following question. What general objectives did all three Republican presidents in the 1920s share?

Fraser: Chapter 22

Complete the following exercises in order *as you read* the chapter.

INTRODUCTION

Introductions provide a valuable guide to the material you are about to read, telling you what topics will be covered and how they fit together. If you keep the "big picture" provided by the introduction in mind as you read the chapter, you'll find it much easier to organize your notes, identify important information, and avoid getting lost in the details. With this in mind, re-read the introduction to Chapter 22. As you read, make a list of the key topics you expect to learn about.

Key Topics

Key Terms

When you finish reading the chapter, identify and explain the importance of the following terms. Use this list to review your understanding of the chapter.

The Coming of the Great Depression

Graphic Note Taking: Charting Key Factors

The Great Depression was sparked by the stock market crash of 1929, and a speculative boom in stock prices was certainly one cause of the depression. Volatility in the stock market, however, was not the only cause of the economic hard times of the 1930s. As you read the section, create a table like the one included below to help you identify the key factors contributing to the crash of the United States economy in 1929. Be sure to note the consequences of each factor you identify. You'll use your table to help you answer a question when you finish the section.

Factor	Consequence

Reviewing the Facts

Provide a short answer (3-4 sentences) for each of the questions below. It's OK if you need to go back and re-read parts of the section in order to find the answers. The purpose of these questions is not to test you, but to help you discover how much you know and what you might need to review.

1. How did the Great Crash of 1929 reflect the typical dynamics of a speculative boom and bust cycle?

2. Why did the practice of buying stock "on margin" make the economic consequences of the crash worse?

3. What underlying weaknesses in the American economy were revealed by the stock market crash?

Making Connections

Take another look at the photograph of crowds on Wall Street on page 665 of your text book. How did the fear created by the stock market crash contribute to the acceleration of the economic crisis that followed?

Graphic Note Taking: Follow Up

Use your notes to answer the following question. In your opinion, what caused the Great Depression?

The New Deal

Graphic Note Taking: Outline

The New Deal represented a major shift in the relationship between the government and the American economy. Where the Republican presidents of the 1920s had seen it as their responsibility to give big business as free a hand as possible, under Franklin Roosevelt the federal government took an active role in all aspects of economic life. As you read the section, create an outline like the one included below to help you trace the development and implementation of the New Deal. You'll use your outline to help you answer a question when you complete the section.

I. The New Deal

    A. The Launch of the New Deal

        1. Roosevelt promised a "New Deal for the American people" during the 1932 campaign

        2. Roosevelt's first priority was to restore confidence in the banking system

        3. Roosevelt used a variety of methods to establish a close relationship with the American people

Reviewing the Facts

Provide a short answer (3-4 sentences) for each of the questions below. It's OK if you need to go back and re-read parts of the section in order to find the answers. The purpose of these questions is not to test you, but to help you discover how much you know and what you might need to review.

1. In what ways did the New Deal reflect prevailing patterns of discrimination against African Americans?

2. What was the goal of the Works Progress Administration (WPA) and what did it accomplish?

3. Compare and contrast the New Deal of 1932 to 1935 with the "Second New Deal."

Making Connections

Take another look at the photograph of Eleanor Roosevelt on page 682 of your text book. What made Eleanor Roosevelt such a valuable political asset for her husband?

Graphic Note Taking: Follow Up

Use your table to answer the following question. In your opinion, was the New Deal a success? Why or why not?

The Deep Roots of War – The United States, Europe, and Asia

Graphic Note Taking: Timeline

The impact of the Great Depression was not limited to economic issues. It also helped touch off dramatic political developments in many parts of the world, developments that would eventually lead to another global war. As you read the section, create a timeline of the 1920s and 1930s marking key events in the march towards war. You'll use timeline table to help you answer a question when you finish the section.

Reviewing the Facts

Provide a short answer (3-4 sentences) for each of the questions below. It's OK if you need to go back and re-read parts of the section in order to find the answers. The purpose of these questions is not to test you, but to help you discover how much you know and what you might need to review.

1. How did developments in the 1920s pave the way for the rise of the Nazi Party to power?

2. How did the Great Depression stimulate Japanese overseas expansion in the 1930s?

3. How did the American public respond to the growing conflict and tensions in Europe and Asia?

Making Connections

Take another look at the photograph of a march for peace on page 686 of your text book. How would

Graphic Note Taking: Follow Up

Use your notes to answer the following question. In your opinion, was a second world war inevitable? Why or why not?

Fraser: Chapter 23

Complete the following exercises in order *as you read* the chapter.

INTRODUCTION

Introductions provide a valuable guide to the material you are about to read, telling you what topics will be covered and how they fit together. If you keep the "big picture" provided by the introduction in mind as you read the chapter, you'll find it much easier to organize your notes, identify important information, and avoid getting lost in the details. With this in mind, re-read the introduction to Chapter 23. As you read, make a list of the key topics you expect to learn about.

Key Topics

Key Terms

When you finish reading the chapter, identify and explain the importance of the following terms. Use this list to review your understanding of the chapter.

Preparedness and Isolation, 1939-1941

Graphic Note Taking: Outline

When France and Britain declared war on Germany in 1939, the United States did not intervene. It was not until December 1941, and the Japanese attack on Pearl Harbor, that America would enter World War II. As you read the section, create an outline like the one included below to help you trace the events that led to U.S. participation in the war. You'll use your outline to help you answer a question when you complete the section.

    I.   Preparedness and Isolation, 1939-1941

        A.   The Battle of Britain

               1.   In May 1940 Germany launched its *Blitzkrieg* on Holland, Belgium, and Luxembourg

               2.   It then turned its attention to France, which quickly fell

               3.   A puppet government, known as Vichy France, was set up under Marshall Philippe Petain

Reviewing the Facts

Provide a short answer (3-4 sentences) for each of the questions below. It's OK if you need to go back and re-read parts of the section in order to find the answers. The purpose of these questions is not to test you, but to help you discover how much you know and what you might need to review.

1. What steps did the Germans take towards control of Europe in 1940?

2. How did military preparations in 1940 and 1941 end the Depression?

3. Why did Japan's leaders decided to attack the United States in 1941?

Making Connections

Take another look at Figure 23-1 on page 695 of your text book. What does it suggest about the economic impact of World War II on the United States?

Graphic Note Taking: Follow Up

Use your notes to answer the following question. How did President Roosevelt support Britain between 1939 and U.S. entry into the war in 1941?

Mass Mobilization in a Society at War

Graphic Note Taking: Compare and Contrast

Once the United States entered the war, the entire society was mobilized. Men and women, military and civilian, all made contributions to the war effort. As you read the section, use a table like the one included below to compare and contrast men and women's service during World War II. Be sure to include contributions made at home and overseas. You'll use your table to help you answer a question when you complete the section.

Men	Women

Reviewing the Facts

Provide a short answer (3-4 sentences) for each of the questions below. It's OK if you need to go back and re-read parts of the section in order to find the answers. The purpose of these questions is not to test you, but to help you discover how much you know and what you might need to review.

1. What new economic opportunities did the war create for women?

2. What was the March on Washington and what did it accomplish?

3. Why were Japanese Americans living on the West Coast treated differently than Japanese-Americans livening in Hawaii?

Making Connections

Take another look at the photograph of female industrial workers on page 702 of your text book. What message might the photographer have meant viewers to take away from this image?

Graphic Note Taking: Follow Up

Use your table to answer the following question. How did the United States entry into World War II change the lives of ordinary men and women?

Industrial Strength, Industrial Prosperity

Graphic Note Taking: Cause and Effect

American leaders quickly realized that if the Allies were going to win the war, America would need to produce vastly more war material than the Axis powers. The massive industrial effort required to achieve this goal ended the depression and brought prosperity to millions of Americans. As you read the section, use a table like the one included below to describe wartime industrial production and to identify the social and economic consequences of that production for the American people. You'll use your table to help you answer a question when you complete the section.

Industrial Production	Wartime Prosperity

Reviewing the Facts

Provide a short answer (3-4 sentences) for each of the questions below. It's OK if you need to go back and re-read parts of the section in order to find the answers. The purpose of these questions is not to test you, but to help you discover how much you know and what you might need to review.

1. How was the U.S. able to produce such an enormous amount of war material in 1942 and 1943?

2. How does the production of Liberty ships illustrate America's approach to military production during World War II?

3. How did the American public and government respond to the early reports about the Holocaust?

Graphic Note Taking: Follow Up

Use your notes to answer the following question. How did the U.S. government pay for the massive industrial effort that was required to win World War II?

Winning a World War – North Africa, Europe, Asia, the Pacific, 1943-1945

Graphic Note Taking: Outline

American industrial might have provided the materials needed to win the war, but the war still needed to be fought. From 1943 to 1945, Americans fought and died around the world to achieve final victory. As you read the section, create an outline like the one included below to help you trace the events that led to the successful conclusion of the war. You'll use your outline to help you answer a question when you complete the section.

    I. Winning a World War – North Africa, Europe, Asia, and the Pacific, 1943 – 1945

        A. The War in Europe, 1943-1945

            1. Russia wanted the Allies to attack the Germans in France to take the pressure off of Russia

            2. Instead, the Allies attacked in North Africa

            3. In January 1943, Roosevelt and Churchill met at Casablanca to plan the next phase of the war

Reviewing the Facts

Provide a short answer (3-4 sentences) for each of the questions below. It's OK if you need to go back and re-read parts of the section in order to find the answers. The purpose of these questions is not to test you, but to help you discover how much you know and what you might need to review.

1. What did the American and Soviet invasion of Germany reveal about the reality and scale of the Holocaust?

2. What strategy did the U.S. employ in the Pacific from 1943 on?

3. What debates within the Truman administration preceded the use of the atomic bomb?

Making Connections

Take another look at the photograph of Nagasaki after the dropping of the atomic bomb on page 718 of your text book. How did images such as this shape the post-war world?

Graphic Note Taking: Follow Up

Use your notes to answer the following question. How did the November 1943 Teheran Conference shape the rest of the war?

Fraser: Chapter 24

Complete the following exercises in order *as you read* the chapter.

INTRODUCTION

Introductions provide a valuable guide to the material you are about to read, telling you what topics will be covered and how they fit together. If you keep the "big picture" provided by the introduction in mind as you read the chapter, you'll find it much easier to organize your notes, identify important information, and avoid getting lost in the details. With this in mind, re-read the introduction to Chapter 24. As you read, make a list of the key topics you expect to learn about.

Key Topics

Key Terms

When you finish reading the chapter, identify and explain the importance of the following terms. Use this list to review your understanding of the chapter.

The United States in 1945 – A Changed Country in a Changed World

Graphic Note Taking: Identifying Key Developments

The world of 1945 was very different from that of 1939. As America made the transition from war to peace, its people and government grappled with change at home and the United States' place in a new world order. As you read the section, use a table like the one included below to take notes on key areas of postwar change. You'll use your table to help you answer a question when you complete the section.

Science and Technology	Returning Soldiers and the Growth of Suburbia	The Great Migration	Immigration	Global Institutions and Markets

Reviewing the Facts

Provide a short answer (3-4 sentences) for each of the questions below. It's OK if you need to go back and re-read parts of the section in order to find the answers. The purpose of these questions is not to test you, but to help you discover how much you know and what you might need to review.

1. How did trends in medicine that began during World War II transform Americans' health during the 1950s?

2. How did the International Harvester cotton picking machine help accelerate African-American migration north?

3. What global institutions were created as a result of the Bretton Woods agreement and what purposes were they meant to serve?

Making Connections

Take another look at the photograph of a suburban kitchen on page 734 of your text book. What does the photograph suggest about expectations for American women in the postwar world?

Graphic Note Taking: Follow Up

Use your notes to answer the following question. What challenges did returning veterans face, and how did the government try to help veterans make the transition back to civilian life?

The Cold War Begins

Graphic Note Taking: Outline

No sooner than one war ended, another one began. The United States and the Soviet Union had been allies during World War II, but tensions were already evident even before World War II was over. As you read the section, create an outline like the one included below to help you trace the emergence of the Cold War, both in foreign and domestic affairs. You'll use your outline to help you answer a question when you complete the section.

    I. The Cold War Begins

          A.   The Hardening of Positions: Containment, the Truman Doctrine, the Marshall Plan, and the Berlin Airlift

                    1.   From the beginning, the United States and the Soviet Union had different goals in World War II

                    2.   The Soviets wanted a buffer zone, control of Eastern Europe, and German machinery and munitions

                    3.   The Americans wanted a rapid recovery of post-war Germany and post-war western Europe in general

Reviewing the Facts

Provide a short answer (3-4 sentences) for each of the questions below. It's OK if you need to go back and re-read parts of the section in order to find the answers. The purpose of these questions is not to test you, but to help you discover how much you know and what you might need to review.

1. Why did George Kennan believe that "containment" of the Soviet Union was necessary?

2. Why did the Soviets blockade Berlin in 1948? How did the U.S. and its allies respond?

3. Who was targeted in the second "Red Scare" that accompanied the beginning of the Cold War?

Making Connections

Take another look at the photograph of an American and a Soviet soldier on page 741 of your text book. Why were scenes like this so quickly a thing of the past?

Graphic Note Taking: Follow Up

Use your notes to answer the following question. Compare and contrast U.S. and Soviet views of developments in Eastern Europe in the years immediately following World War II.

Politics, 1948 and 1952

Graphic Note Taking: Compare and Contrast

In 1948, Harry Truman pulled out a surprise victory over his Republican opponent. By 1952, however, the nation was ready to give the Republicans control of the White House for the first time since 1928. As you read the section, use a table like the one included below to compare and contrast the political situation in 1948 and 1952. You'll use your table to help you answer a question when you complete the section.

1948	1952

Reviewing the Facts

Provide a short answer (3-4 sentences) for each of the questions below. It's OK if you need to go back and re-read parts of the section in order to find the answers. The purpose of these questions is not to test you, but to help you discover how much you know and what you might need to review.

1. How did Congress defeat Truman's effort to continue Roosevelt's domestic policy agenda?

2. What steps did President Truman take to counter racial discrimination and segregation?

3. What did Eisenhower mean by "Modern Republicanism"?

Making Connections

Take another look at the photograph of a triumphant Truman on page 756 of your text book. Why were so many people convinced that Truman would lose in 1948?

Graphic Note Taking: Follow Up

Use your table to answer the following question. What factors contributed to Republican victory in 1952?

Fraser: Chapter 25

Complete the following exercises in order *as you read* the chapter.

INTRODUCTION

Introductions provide a valuable guide to the material you are about to read, telling you what topics will be covered and how they fit together. If you keep the "big picture" provided by the introduction in mind as you read the chapter, you'll find it much easier to organize your notes, identify important information, and avoid getting lost in the details. With this in mind, re-read the introduction to Chapter 25. As you read, make a list of the key topics you expect to learn about.

Key Topics

Key Terms

When you finish reading the chapter, identify and explain the importance of the following terms. Use this list to review your understanding of the chapter.

Eisenhower's America, America's World

Graphic Note Taking: Outline

Throughout the 1950s, President Eisenhower and his advisors tried to a craft a foreign policy that would meet America's needs, respond to the challenges of a nuclear world, and cost as little as possible. As you read the section, create an outline like the one included below to help you trace the development of American foreign policy in the 1950s. You'll use your outline to help you answer a question when you complete the section.

    I. Eisenhower's America, America's World

        A.   Foreign Policy and the Hydrogen Bomb

               1.   Despite Eisenhower's efforts, the United States and the Soviet Union were locked in a conventional and nuclear arms race.

               2.   Eisenhower's foreign policy had two key components: a policy of massive retaliation and the use of covert forces.

               3.   In 1953, the CIA organized a coup against the elected Prime Minister of Iran.

Reviewing the Facts

Provide a short answer (3-4 sentences) for each of the questions below. It's OK if you need to go back and re-read parts of the section in order to find the answers. The purpose of these questions is not to test you, but to help you discover how much you know and what you might need to review.

1. How and why did the United States intervene in Iran in the 1950s?

2. What steps did Eisenhower take to reduce tensions with the Soviet Union in his second term? What ultimately undermined his efforts?

3. What strengths helped John F. Kennedy win the 1960 election?

Making Connections

Take another look at the photograph of Sputnik on page 767 of your text book. Why did the successful launch of this tiny satellite cause such concern in the United States?

Graphic Note Taking: Follow Up

Use your outline to answer the following question. What was the policy of massive retaliation and what objectives was it meant to help accomplish?

A Culture on the Move

Graphic Note Taking: Identifying Key Trends

The 1950s were a period of unprecedented prosperity in the United States, a fact that was reflected in the culture of the decade. As you read the section, use a table like the one included below to take notes on four important elements of that culture: television, automobiles, organized religion, and dissent. You'll use your table to help you answer a question when you complete the section.

Television	Automobiles	Organized Religion	Dissent

Reviewing the Facts

Provide a short answer (3-4 sentences) for each of the questions below. It's OK if you need to go back and re-read parts of the section in order to find the answers. The purpose of these questions is not to test you, but to help you discover how much you know and what you might need to review.

1. Why kinds of programs were featured on 1950s television?

2. What trends in American participation in organized religion emerged in the 1950s?

3. How did Alfred Kinsey's work challenge commonly held assumptions about American sexual practices?

Making Connections

Take another look at the photograph of an American family watching television on page 770 of your text book. What social values might the photographer have hoped to convey through this image?

Graphic Note Taking: Follow Up

Use your table to answer the following question. What impact did the boom in automobile ownership have on American society and culture?

Race and Civil Rights

Graphic Note Taking: Mastering Details

The fight to end racial segregation and discrimination did not begin in the 1950s, but it was in that decade that the Civil Rights movement came of age. As you read the section, make a list of key events in the civil rights struggle of the 1950s and early 1960s. Be sure to note the importance of each event you include in your list. You'll use your list to help you answer a question when you complete the section.

1.

2.

3.

4.

5.

6.

7.

Reviewing the Facts

Provide a short answer (3-4 sentences) for each of the questions below. It's OK if you need to go back and re-read parts of the section in order to find the answers. The purpose of these questions is not to test you, but to help you discover how much you know and what you might need to review.

1. What NAACP court victories in the 1930s and 1940s paved the way for *Brown v. Board of Education*?

2. What do the sit-ins of the early 1960s reveal about generational divisions within the civil rights movement?

3. How did the hopes of blacks in the South differ from those of blacks in the North?

Making Connections

Take another look at the photograph of the arrest of Rosa Parks on page 781 of your text book. What made Parks such an ideal candidate to challenge segregation in Montgomery?

Graphic Note Taking: Follow Up

Use your list to answer the following question. How did southern whites respond in the 1950s and early 1960s to intensified civil rights activity and to Supreme Court rulings that overturned segregation and challenged racial discrimination?

Fraser: Chapter 26

Complete the following exercises in order *as you read* the chapter.

INTRODUCTION

Introductions provide a valuable guide to the material you are about to read, telling you what topics will be covered and how they fit together. If you keep the "big picture" provided by the introduction in mind as you read the chapter, you'll find it much easier to organize your notes, identify important information, and avoid getting lost in the details. With this in mind, re-read the introduction to Chapter 26. As you read, make a list of the key topics you expect to learn about.

Key Topics

Key Terms

When you finish reading the chapter, identify and explain the importance of the following terms. Use this list to review your understanding of the chapter.

New Voices, New Authorities

Graphic Note Taking: Outline

The conformity of the 1950s masked the growing discontent of many Americans, particularly younger Americans, with the social and political status quo. In the early 1960s, that discontent exploded in new political movements and new forms of cultural expression. As you read the section, create an outline like the one included below to help you understand the nature of popular protest and dissent in the early 1960s. You'll use your outline to help you answer a question when you complete the section.

I. New Voices, New Authorities

    A.   Books, Films, Music

        1.   Jane Jacob's *The Death and Life of Great American Cities* had a profound effect on subsequent urban planning.

        2.   Rachel Carson's *Silent Spring* played a key role in inspiring the modern environmental movement.

        3.   Michael Harrington's *The Other America* helped inspire the Kennedy-Johnson War on Poverty.

Reviewing the Facts

Provide a short answer (3-4 sentences) for each of the questions below. It's OK if you need to go back and re-read parts of the section in order to find the answers. The purpose of these questions is not to test you, but to help you discover how much you know and what you might need to review.

1. How did Rachel Carson's *Silent Spring* differ from earlier environmental works?

2. Why did Michael Harrington's *The Other America* have such large impact on public policy?

3. What trends in higher education help explain why universities were centers of political protest in the 1960s?

Making Connections

Take another look at the photograph of Joan Baez and Bob Dylan on page 797 of your text book. What trends in American culture were reflected in the popularity of folk music, particularly politically charged folk music?

Graphic Note Taking: Follow Up

Use your outline to answer the following question. What role did students play in the protest movements of the 1960s?

Camelot, the White House, and Dallas — The Kennedy Administration

Graphic Note Taking: Timeline

John F. Kennedy's assassination cut short his presidency and denied him the opportunity to serve a second term. Nonetheless, the Kennedy administration marked an important turning point in American history. As you read the section, create a timeline of key events during the Kennedy administration. You'll use your timeline to help you answer a question when you complete the section.

Reviewing the Facts

Provide a short answer (3-4 sentences) for each of the questions below. It's OK if you need to go back and re-read parts of the section in order to find the answers. The purpose of these questions is not to test you, but to help you discover how much you know and what you might need to review.

1. Why, despite his promises, was Kennedy slow to move on civil rights?

2. What did the Supreme Court rule in *Abington School Board v. Schempp* and why was the ruling so controversial?

3. What were the terms of the agreement that ended the Cuban missile crisis?

Making Connections

Take another look at the photograph of John and Jacqueline Kennedy on page 800 of your text book. What qualities did the American public associate with the president and first lady?

Graphic Note Taking: Follow Up

Use your timeline to answer the following question. In your opinion, was John F. Kennedy a great president? Why or why not?

The Coming of Lyndon B. Johnson

Graphic Note Taking: Mastering Details

Lyndon Johnson enjoyed broad popular support in his first few years in office, support he used to pass a wide variety of social legislation. As you read the section, make a list of Johnson's most important legislative accomplishments. Be sure to note the importance of each law you include in your list. You'll use your list to help you answer a question when you complete the section.

1.

2.

3.

4.

5.

6.

Reviewing the Facts

Provide a short answer (3-4 sentences) for each of the questions below. It's OK if you need to go back and re-read parts of the section in order to find the answers. The purpose of these questions is not to test you, but to help you discover how much you know and what you might need to review.

1. What explains Johnson's extraordinary success in passing his domestic agenda through Congress?

2. How did the Johnson administration expand access to health care?

3. Why did Johnson think it necessary to escalate American involvement in Vietnam?

Making Connections

Take another look at the photograph of Huey P. Newton and Bobby Seale on page 821 of your text book. Why did so many Americans, particularly white Americans, find images like this one so frightening?

Graphic Note Taking: Follow Up

Use your list to answer the following question. Judged solely on his domestic record, should Lyndon Johnson be considered a great president? Why or why not?

Fraser: Chapter 27

Complete the following exercises in order *as you read* the chapter.

INTRODUCTION

Introductions provide a valuable guide to the material you are about to read, telling you what topics will be covered and how they fit together. If you keep the "big picture" provided by the introduction in mind as you read the chapter, you'll find it much easier to organize your notes, identify important information, and avoid getting lost in the details. With this in mind, re-read the introduction to Chapter 27. As you read, make a list of the key topics you expect to learn about.

Key Topics

Key Terms

When you finish reading the chapter, identify and explain the importance of the following terms. Use this list to review your understanding of the chapter.

The New Politics of the Late 1960s

Graphic Note Taking: Identifying an Agenda

While Richard Nixon made his reputation in politics as an arch-conservative, his policies as president were decidedly centrist. On the domestic front he supported legislation that had broad Democratic support, and his most important foreign policy accomplishment was normalizing relations with communist China. As you read the section, take notes on the Nixon administration's policies in a table like the one included below. You'll use your table to help you answer a question when you complete the section.

Domestic Policy	Foreign Policy

Reviewing the Facts

Provide a short answer (3-4 sentences) for each of the questions below. It's OK if you need to go back and re-read parts of the section in order to find the answers. The purpose of these questions is not to test you, but to help you discover how much you know and what you might need to review.

1. How did the ideological divisions within American politics change after 1960?

2. How did Nixon respond to growing calls for greater environmental protection?

3. What did Nixon gain from his trip to China? What China gain from Nixon's visit?

Making Connections

Take another look at the photograph of Nixon in China on page 832 of your text book. Why would such a picture have seemed inconceivable to most Americans ten years earlier?

Graphic Note Taking: Follow Up

Use your table to answer the following question. Is it fair to describe Nixon's domestic record as "liberal"? Why or why not?

The Movements of the 1960s and 1970s

Graphic Note Taking: Mastering the Details

In the wake of the Civil Rights Movement of the 1950s and 1960s, a wide variety of groups formed their own movements to demand greater rights and greater inclusion in American society. As you read the section, make a list of these new movements. Be sure to note the primary objectives of each group you included in your list. You'll use your list to help you answer a question when you complete the section.

1.

2.

3.

4.

5.

6.

7.

Reviewing the Facts

Provide a short answer (3-4 sentences) for each of the questions below. It's OK if you need to go back and re-read parts of the section in order to find the answers. The purpose of these questions is not to test you, but to help you discover how much you know and what you might need to review.

1. What kind of reception did the Equal Rights Amendment (ERA) receive when it was presented to Congress for consideration in 1969? Why were supporters confident of its eventual ratification?

2. What concrete advances did Indian protests help secure?

3. How did access to higher education become an important focus of the debate over racial equality in the 1970s?

Making Connections

Take another look at the photograph of women's rights protestors on page 834 of your text book. How did the goals of such protestors differ from those of earlier women's rights advocates?

Graphic Note Taking: Follow Up

Use your list to answer the following question. How were the social movements of the late 1960s inspired by the strategies and goals of the Civil Rights Movement?

The Culture Wars of the 1970s

Graphic Note Taking: Mastering Details

The 1970s saw the emergence of a strong backlash against the social and cultural movements of the 1960s. Anti-feminist organizations emerged and the conservative religious organizations became a powerful new force in politics. As you read the section, create an outline like the one included below to help you understand the nature of this backlash. You'll use your outline to help you answer a question when you complete the section.

I. The Culture Wars of the 1970s

    A. Phyllis Schlafly and the Defeat of the Equal Rights Amendment

        1. Schlafly was leading Republican Party activist and supporter of Barry Goldwater

        2. Launched the STOP ERA movement

        3. Campaign against ERA fits within framework of 1970s cultural conservatism

Reviewing the Facts

Provide a short answer (3-4 sentences) for each of the questions below. It's OK if you need to go back and re-read parts of the section in order to find the answers. The purpose of these questions is not to test you, but to help you discover how much you know and what you might need to review.

1. What cultural issues moved to the center of conservative political debate in the 1970s?

2. What was the Moral Majority and what did it stand for?

Making Connections

Take another look at Map 27-1 Support and Opposition to the ERA on page 842 of your text book. What does the map tell you about the regional nature of the cultural divide in the 1970s?

Graphic Note Taking: Follow Up

Use your outline to answer the following question. How did the rise of cultural conservatism in the 1970s reshape American politics?

Politics, Economics, and the Impact of Watergate

Graphic Note Taking: Timeline

Watergate, a faltering economy, and the rise of cultural conservatism all shaped national politics in the 1970s. As you read the section, create a timeline of key events in 1970s national politics. You'll use your timeline to help you answer a question when you complete the section.

Reviewing the Facts

Provide a short answer (3-4 sentences) for each of the questions below. It's OK if you need to go back and re-read parts of the section in order to find the answers. The purpose of these questions is not to test you, but to help you discover how much you know and what you might need to review.

1. What was "stagflation" and why did it emerge in the early 1970s?

2. How Gerald Ford justify his pardon of Richard Nixon?

3. How did Jimmy Carter respond to the economic problems that plagued the United States in the 1970s?

Making Connections

Take another look at the photograph of American hostages on page 853 of your text book. Why did images like this strike such a powerful chord with American's in the late 1970s?

Graphic Note Taking: Follow Up

Use your timeline to answer the following question. How did the rising price of oil affect the American economy and American politics in the 1970s?

Fraser: Chapter 28

Complete the following exercises in order *as you read* the chapter.

INTRODUCTION

Introductions provide a valuable guide to the material you are about to read, telling you what topics will be covered and how they fit together. If you keep the "big picture" provided by the introduction in mind as you read the chapter, you'll find it much easier to organize your notes, identify important information, and avoid getting lost in the details. With this in mind, re-read the introduction to Chapter 28. As you read, make a list of the key topics you expect to learn about.

Key Topics

Key Terms

When you finish reading the chapter, identify and explain the importance of the following terms. Use this list to review your understanding of the chapter.

A Rapidly Changing U.S. Government

Graphic Note Taking: Identifying an Agenda

Ronald Reagan oversaw a change in American government. His domestic policies changed the relationship of the federal government to American society. In foreign affairs, Reagan pursued an intensified anti-communist agenda. His successor, George H.W. Bush, was president when the Cold War came to an end. As you read the section, take notes on the Reagan administration's policies in a table like the one included below. You'll use your table to help you answer a question when you complete the section.

Domestic Policy	Foreign Policy

Reviewing the Facts

Provide a short answer (3-4 sentences) for each of the questions below. It's OK if you need to go back and re-read parts of the section in order to find the answers. The purpose of these questions is not to test you, but to help you discover how much you know and what you might need to review.

1. What domestic policy goals did Reagan achieve in his first term?

2. How did Reagan work to undermine the power of American unions?

3. What doubts did critics have about the Strategic Defense Initiative (SDI)? Who supported the initiative and why?

Making Connections

Take another look at the photograph of older Americans protesting Reagan's cuts to social programs on page 865 of your text book. How would you explain the failure of such protests to impact public policy?

Graphic Note Taking: Follow Up

Use your table to answer the following question. What core assumptions underlay Reagan's economic policies?

The Changing Nature of the American Economy

Graphic Note Taking: Mastering the Details

As important components of Reaganomics were put into practice, a growing debate emerged about their impact on the American economy and on American society. As you read the section, create an outline like the one included below to help you understand impact of Reaganomics. You'll use your outline to help you answer a question when you complete the section.

    I. The Changing Nature of the American Economy

        A.   Reagan's Economic Bill of Rights

             1.   Freedom to work

             2.   Freedom to enjoy the fruits of ones labor

             3.   Freedom to own and control one's property

             4.   Freedom to participate in a free market

Reviewing the Facts

Provide a short answer (3-4 sentences) for each of the questions below. It's OK if you need to go back and re-read parts of the section in order to find the answers. The purpose of these questions is not to test you, but to help you discover how much you know and what you might need to review.

1. What freedoms were included in Reagan's "Economic Bill of Rights"?

2. What economic trends were embodied in the career of Michael Milken?

3. How did Reagan's efforts at deregulation contribute to the collapse of the nation's savings and loan industry?

Making Connections

Take another look at Figure 28-1: Real Family Income, 1980-1990 on page 878 of your text book. What major social and economic trends do the charts reveal?

Graphic Note Taking: Follow Up

Use your outline to answer the following question. In your opinion, on the whole, was the implementation of Reaganomics a good or bad thing for the country? Why?

Changes in the Rest of the Country

Graphic Note Taking: Mastering Details

The 1980's were a decade of significant cultural change, as globalization took hold and the nation grew more diverse. For some Americans, these changes were a cause for celebration. For others, particularly religious conservatives, these changes represented a threat to traditional American values. As you read the section, create an outline like the one included below to help you understand cultural change in the 1980s and the reaction to it. You'll use your outline to help you answer a question when you complete the section.

I. Changes in the Rest of the Country

    A.   Popular Culture – Music and Television

        1.   American popular music had come to dominate the world

        2.   This was made possible in part by rapidly changing information formats and technology

        3.   As was the case in earlier generations, the popular music of the 1980s represented a challenge to traditional culture and its music

Reviewing the Facts

Provide a short answer (3-4 sentences) for each of the questions below. It's OK if you need to go back and re-read parts of the section in order to find the answers. The purpose of these questions is not to test you, but to help you discover how much you know and what you might need to review.

1. What was the Religious Right and what made its members politically powerful?

2. How did immigration between 1970 and 2000 differ from that of earlier eras?

3. How did the Reagan administration respond to the emergence and spread of HIV-AIDS?

Making Connections

Take another look at the photograph of a leader in the anti-abortion movement on page 883 of your text book. How would you explain the fact that abortion became of a central focus of conservative activism in the 1980s?

Graphic Note Taking: Follow Up

Use your outline to answer the following question. Why did debates over immigration intensify in the 1980s?

Fraser: Chapter 29

Complete the following exercises in order *as you read* the chapter.

INTRODUCTION

Introductions provide a valuable guide to the material you are about to read, telling you what topics will be covered and how they fit together. If you keep the "big picture" provided by the introduction in mind as you read the chapter, you'll find it much easier to organize your notes, identify important information, and avoid getting lost in the details. With this in mind, re-read the introduction to Chapter 29. As you read, make a list of the key topics you expect to learn about.

Key Topics

Key Terms

When you finish reading the chapter, identify and explain the importance of the following terms. Use this list to review your understanding of the chapter.

The Bush Administration, 1989-1993

Graphic Note Taking: Identifying an Agenda

George H.W. Bush's experience prior to becoming president prepared him well to direct America's foreign policy as the Cold War wound down and new challenges emerged in the Middle East. He was, however, less skillful in responding to domestic challenges. As you read the section, take notes on the Bush administration's policies in a table like the one included below. You'll use your table to help you answer a question when you complete the section.

Domestic Policy	Foreign Policy

Reviewing the Facts

Provide a short answer (3-4 sentences) for each of the questions below. It's OK if you need to go back and re-read parts of the section in order to find the answers. The purpose of these questions is not to test you, but to help you discover how much you know and what you might need to review.

1. What steps did George H.W. Bush take to gain international support for reversing Iraq's occupation of Kuwait?

2. Why was the nomination of Clarence Thomas to the Supreme Court so controversial?

3. How did economic issues undermine the Bush administration?

Making Connections

Take another look at the photograph of American troops entering Kuwait on page 895 of your text book.

Why did Bush decide not to follow up the swift military victory in Kuwait with an invasion of Iraq?

Graphic Note Taking: Follow Up

Use your table to answer the following question. In your opinion, did George H.W. Bush deserve to be elected to a second term? Why or why not?

The Clinton Presidency

Graphic Note Taking: Timeline

The Clinton administration achieved many of its policy goals and benefitted from a robust economy. Nonetheless, mistakes, scandal, and the determined opposition of conservative Republicans undermined the administration's effectiveness. As you read the section, create a timeline to help you identify the most important events of the Clinton presidency. You'll use your timeline to help you answer a question when you complete the section.

Reviewing the Facts

Provide a short answer (3-4 sentences) for each of the questions below. It's OK if you need to go back and re-read parts of the section in order to find the answers. The purpose of these questions is not to test you, but to help you discover how much you know and what you might need to review.

1. Why did Clinton's efforts to reform the nation's healthcare fail?

2. What were the causes and consequences of the government shutdown of 1995-1996?

3. How did the American public respond to the Clinton-Lewinsky scandal? Why did it react as it did?

Making Connections

Take another look at the photograph of a young anti-NAFTA protestor on page 901 of your text book. What groups in American society were most opposed to NAFTA? Why?

Graphic Note Taking: Follow Up

Use your timeline to help you answer the following question. How and why did Clinton co-opt Republican policy positions?

Technology Dominates an Era

Graphic Note Taking: Outline

The 1990s saw the widespread adoption of new and groundbreaking information technologies. It quickly became clear that these technologies would alter the relationships Americans had with each other, as well as America's relationship to the rest of the world. As you read the section, create an outline like the one included below to help you understand the impact of new technologies in the 1990s. You'll use your outline to help you answer a question when you complete the section.

I. Technology Dominates an Era

    A.   The Birth of New Technologies

        1.   The first computers were developed for military applications during World War II

        2.   Mainframe computers gained acceptance in American industry over the course of the 1950s and 1960s

        3.   A series of postwar inventions contributed to the invention of the personal computer

Reviewing the Facts

Provide a short answer (3-4 sentences) for each of the questions below. It's OK if you need to go back and re-read parts of the section in order to find the answers. The purpose of these questions is not to test you, but to help you discover how much you know and what you might need to review.

1. What was the very first personal computer like and to whom was it marketed?

2. What prompted the invention of the first version of the Internet?

3. How did innovations in information technology harm the music industry?

Making Connections

Take another look at the photograph of a search engine advertisement on page 917 of your text book. How have search engines such as the one developed by Google changed your student-experience? How do you use them in the context of your classes?

Graphic Note Taking: Follow Up

Use your outline to answer the following question. In your opinion, does the introduction of new technologies in the late twentieth and early twentieth century constitute a shift as dramatic as that produced by the Industrial Revolution? Why or why not?

Fraser: Chapter 30

Complete the following exercises in order *as you read* the chapter.

INTRODUCTION

Introductions provide a valuable guide to the material you are about to read, telling you what topics will be covered and how they fit together. If you keep the "big picture" provided by the introduction in mind as you read the chapter, you'll find it much easier to organize your notes, identify important information, and avoid getting lost in the details. With this in mind, re-read the introduction to Chapter 30. As you read, make a list of the key topics you expect to learn about.

Key Topics

Key Terms

When you finish reading the chapter, identify and explain the importance of the following terms. Use this list to review your understanding of the chapter.

The Impact of September 11, 2001

Graphic Note Taking: Timeline

September 11, 2001 marked a decisive turning point in American history. The terrorist attacks that occurred that day produced important shifts in foreign policy, governmental power, and Americans' perceptions of themselves and the world. As you read the section, create a timeline to help you identify the most important events that followed in the wake of the 9/11 attacks. You'll use your timeline to help you answer a question when you complete the section.

Reviewing the Facts

Provide a short answer (3-4 sentences) for each of the questions below. It's OK if you need to go back and re-read parts of the section in order to find the answers. The purpose of these questions is not to test you, but to help you discover how much you know and what you might need to review.

1. What were the major findings of the 9/11 commission?

2. What were the most important terms of the USA PATRIOT Act?

3. What assumptions guided U.S. policy in the immediate aftermath of the invasion of Iraq?

Making Connections

Take another look at the photograph of the ruins of the World Trade Center on page 924 of your text book. What memories do you have of 9/11? Did the event change the way you see America and its place in the world?

Graphic Note Taking: Follow Up

Use your timeline to answer the following question. In your opinion, did the U.S. government strike the right balance between individual civil liberties and national security in the years following 9/11? Why or why not?

Hurricane Katrina and Its Aftermath

Graphic Note Taking: Cause and Effect

Hurricane Katrina was a natural disaster, but the loss of life and destruction of property it produced were made worse by human actions. As you read the section, create a table like the one included below to help you understand how decisions made prior to 2005 compounded the damage it inflicted. You'll use your table to help you answer a question when you complete the section.

Pre-Hurricane Actions and Policies	Consequences

Reviewing the Facts

Provide a short answer (3-4 sentences) for each of the questions below. It's OK if you need to go back and re-read parts of the section in order to find the answers. The purpose of these questions is not to test you, but to help you discover how much you know and what you might need to review.

1. What government failures led to large numbers of people being trapped in New Orleans when Hurricane Katrina hit?

2. What kind of destruction did Hurricane Katrina produce in New Orleans?

3. What problems and failures plagued the post-hurricane clean up?

Making Connections

Take another look at the photograph of flooding in the Ninth ward following Hurricane Katrina on page 936 of your text book. In your opinion, what are the implications of the fact that most of the people trapped in New Orleans during Hurricane Katrina were poor and black?

Graphic Note Taking: Follow Up

Use your table to help you answer the following question. In your opinion, what were the most important lessons of Hurricane Katrina and its aftermath?

The Financial Crisis of 2008

Graphic Note Taking: Causes and Consequences

The financial crisis that struck in 2008 and set off a deep and lasting recession caught most observers by surprise. Once the crisis hit, a spirited debate emerged about its causes. What were undebatable, however, were its devastating consequences. As you read the section, create a table like the one included below to help you understand the causes and consequences of the financial crisis of 2008. You'll use your table to help you answer a question when you complete the section.

Causes	Consequences

Reviewing the Facts

Provide a short answer (3-4 sentences) for each of the questions below. It's OK if you need to go back and re-read parts of the section in order to find the answers. The purpose of these questions is not to test you, but to help you discover how much you know and what you might need to review.

1. How did deregulation contribute to the financial crisis of 2008?

2. In the immediate aftermath of the financial crisis, who was blamed for causing it?

3. How did the U.S. economy fair in the years following 2008?

Making Connections

Take another look at the photograph of a foreclosed property on page 939 of your text book. In your opinion, who should take primary responsibility for the housing bubble that preceded the financial crisis of 2008? Homeowners, lenders, investment houses, the government? Why?

Graphic Note Taking: Follow Up

Use your table to answer the following question. In your opinion, who or what was responsible for the financial crisis of 2008?

New Liberals, New Conservatives

Graphic Note Taking: Outline

When Barrack Obama was elected president in November, 2008, the country faced a number of major challenges, perhaps the most important being the ongoing fallout from the financial crisis that had begun some months earlier. Over the course of Obama's presidency, new political groups and ideologies emerged in reaction to the problems that plagued the country and the government's response to them. As you read the section, create an outline like the one included below to help you understand the major currents in American politics during the Obama administration. You'll use your outline to help you answer a question when you complete the section.

    I. New Liberals, New Conservatives

        A. The Unprecedented Election of 2008

                1. Harry Reid urged Obama to run for president because he feared the consequences of Hillary Clinton becoming the nominee

                2. Obama used a sophisticated campaign to defeat Clinton and gain the nomination

                3. Obama's opponent, John McCain, emerged as the Republican nominee after a bruising primary battle

Reviewing the Facts

Provide a short answer (3-4 sentences) for each of the questions below. It's OK if you need to go back and re-read parts of the section in order to find the answers. The purpose of these questions is not to test you, but to help you discover how much you know and what you might need to review.

1. What were the main provisions of the Patient Protection and Affordable Healthcare Act?

2. What general concerns and opinions united Tea Party members?

3. What strengths and weaknesses did Obama have as he began the 2012 campaign?

Making Connections

Take another look at the photograph of a Tea Party March on page 945 of your text book. In your opinion, what is the root cause of political anger in early twenty-first century America? Do the Tea Party and Occupy movements have anything in common?

Graphic Note Taking: Follow Up

Use your outline to answer the following questions. In your opinion, what is the most important problem facing the United States in the early twenty-first century? What role, if any, should the government take in helping to solve this problem? What other groups must also be involved?